Spark Jr:

Creative Writing Prompts
for
Young Adults

DUSTY DURSTON

Published By: Novel Treasure Publishing LLC

Visit our website at www.noveltreasurepublishing.com

Edited By: Nicole d'Entremont

Cover Designed By: Miblart

Designer Website: www.miblart.com

ISBN 13: 978-1-951625-04-7

ACKNOWLEDGMENTS

A big thank you to Dixie Wingate for all the support she gives me. She is my power source when I am low, my cheerleader when I am running strong, and my shoulder to cry on when I am feeling overwhelmed.

Thank you, Mom, for listening to all my wild ideas as I am running with them.

Thank you, Wade Mummert, for helping me handle my life when I can't.

Thank you, Douglas Durston II, for making me laugh.

DEDICATION

To my children, Caden and Stephanie.

OTHER BOOKS BY AUTHOR

IGNITE

SPARK

HOW TO USE THIS BOOK

Spark Jr. is designed as a tool for anyone who enjoys creative writing exercises. These exercises are ideal for teachers or homeschooling parents looking to integrate vocabulary words and add excitement to their writing lessons or for young writers needing story inspiration. These writing prompts are a mixture of genre's, appropriate for middle grade and higher.

This is a collection of 40 individual scenes that include specific vocab words designed to spark creative thought. Each scene gives you just enough detail to make you question what is going on, how and why the situation is happening, and who the characters are.

Read a scene and let your imagination run wild, filling in the gaps that are purposely left open for you to finish. Put yourself in one of the character's shoes and feel their laughter, sorrow, frustration, and more.

Answer the questions at the end of each story to dive deeper into the lives of a character you're not familiar with, and you will find yourself breathing life into your own stories.

HAPPY WRITING!

TABLE OF CONTENTS

TABLE OF CONTENTS

CHAPTER 1
THE NOTE
(Bewildered)

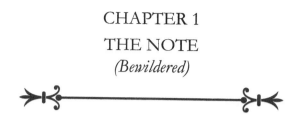

On a typical day, Alex would be riding his bike to school at this very moment. But, today was different. He was sitting inside The Coffee King, a coffee shop he'd passed by a thousand times before.

The Coffee King was the only shop in town that sold Hawaiian fruit coffee. A blinking neon sign said it was the best coffee in town. Alex would beg to differ; the stench of it wafting out the door and onto the sidewalk always forced him to ride his bike on the other side of the street.

Sitting in a wobbly chair with his back to the wall, he could see everyone coming and going, precisely his plan. He couldn't leave until he knew who wrote him the note. A new pot of coffee was brewing, making his stomach brew and churn, also not a pleasant feeling.

Alex imagined barfing all over the table. Would I get up and leave if I barfed? Nope. Even if I barf, I'm not going anywhere. I have to see who this note is from and what they want. Sooner or later, he would recognize the person entering the cafe.

Alex's eyes frequently shifted from the door to the waiter, who was eyeballing him hard. Two churns in his stomach and then a horrible thought ran through his mind.

Maybe it was the waiter! But how could he get to my backpack at school? I'm getting more paranoid by the second. He's probably just annoyed because I didn't order anything.

Alex pushed the thought of the waiter out of his head and pulled the note from his backpack.

The handwriting was neat but not too neat. It wasn't loopy and curly like the handwriting from some of the girls he knew. It definitely wasn't like any of his guy friends; their writing was almost unreadable.

Maybe it was a teacher's handwriting? Teachers wrote neatly. Most teacher's handwriting he saw, was cursive though. This wasn't cursive, but it was neat. The kind of neat that happens when someone takes their time writing every single letter very carefully.

Maybe he'd missed something on the back, he thought. He flipped the letter over, still blank. No secret codes popped up to fill Alex in. A long sigh escaped him, and at that very moment, he realized someone was standing in front of him.

His heart pounded. He swallowed hard. His eyes widened as they raised.

"Kid," the waiter spurted out.

Alex's heart was pounding so hard he couldn't immediately respond.

"You ok?" the waiter asked.

"You just scared me," Alex panted.

"You need to order something if you want to stay here," the waiter said.

"Oh, okay. Well, I have a dollar. What can I get with that?" Alex asked.

"Nothing," the waiter said, clearly irritated with him. "What are you doing here?"

"I'm waiting for someone," Alex said.

"I have a feeling you're also late for school. You've got five more minutes, then you need to scram," the waiter said and walked away.

"Okay," Alex said.

The corners of Alex's mouth turned down slightly as he began to read the note for the hundredth time.

YOUR TURN:

1. If Alex is missing school, the message on this note must be very important or very mysterious. What do you think was on the letter and why?

2. Why was Alex at The Coffee King?

3. Using your answers from question one and two, write the note that would make Alex miss school.

4. Define the word bewildered. Is Alex bewildered, or is there a better word? Explain your answer.

5. Using your answers from above, finish the story.

CHAPTER 2
BOORISH LIBRARIAN
(Desolate)

Polly knew that her chair was a bit screechy, but she was trying her hardest to be still.

Screeeeeeech.

Polly sat stiffly, waiting to see if anyone had heard.

A piece of waded up paper smacked her in the side of the head, rolled down her arm, and fell to its death next to her foot.

Polly looked down to see if there was anything distinguishable on it. She dared not move her head too much, or the shift in weight could trigger the obnoxious shrill shriek she was desperately trying to avoid. The last thing she wanted to do was bring Mrs. Clatterbun, the librarian, racing back over to shush her and threaten detention.

There was a familiarity with the paper. Blue ink from a graphic shown through. She'd seen that blue before, but where? Her eyes tried to pierce the paper and decode the puzzle. She didn't dare to get a closer look. She couldn't take any chances. Her chair was just waiting for another reason to get attention.

Hearing shuffling from behind, her ears perked up, but she maintained the super freeze position she had going on. Not wanting to draw attention to herself, she fought the urge to turn her head to get into a better listening position. From this position, she could not see the events occurring one isle over.

Small font at the edge of the computer read 2:58 pm. Only two more minutes, and she could be as loud as she wanted. That paper would be in her hands, and she could figure out who threw it at her, and better yet, why.

"Your research paper isn't finishing itself, Polly," came a cackling voice from over her left shoulder.

Another quick screech escaped the chair as she jerked in surprise. "Yes, Mrs. Clatterbun."

"What's this piece of paper doing on the floor?" Mrs. Clatterbun asked. "Is it yours?"

"No," Polly said. "But…"

"Trash, trash, trashy kids," Mrs. Clatterbun murmured under her breath as she picked up the wad of paper and took it with her.

Ding, ding, dong…

The bell rang, and Polly's chair sounded like it was being murdered as she swung around. "Mrs. Clatterbun, I'll take that paper," Polly yelled.

Mrs. Clatterbun was gone. Vanished more like it. *How could she have disappeared so quickly?* Polly thought. *Sneaking up on kids was her specialty, so maybe sneaking away was too.*

Polly grabbed her purple and blue backpack from the floor and headed towards Mrs. Clatterbun's desk.

A little bell sat on the librarian's desk. Odd. Everyone was supposed to be so quiet every single second inside the library, but they had the most annoyingly loud bell to ring for help. Oh well, it wasn't what Polly wanted to spend her time thinking about. She wanted to get that paper.

She peered around the desk and saw a trash can ready to be scavenged. A quick look inside determined that gum collected from all the mouths throughout the day were the only things in that trash can.

After scanning the library aisles a few times, she turned back around to the desk and put her hand above the bell. Normally she would have smacked that bell twice, but this time she hesitated. Her hand hovered above the bell, not moving. Polly stood still while her brain began to catch up to what she had just seen behind her.

It was something she had never seen before. It was deep and dark and empty. Absolute silence filled the library: no whispers, no squeaky chairs, no carts with books moving between the aisles. No people.

Polly slowly lowered her hand and turned around.

A screech came from where she was sitting earlier, and Polly yelled. "Who's there!"

YOUR TURN:

1. Would you have tempted fate and picked up the paper (possibly getting detention), or would you have left the paper on the ground and tried to wait out the two minutes?

2. Write what was on the crumpled-up paper.

3. Why or how did all the people disappear so quickly? Is it connected to the note?

4. Define the word desolate. Does this word properly define Polly in the library? Explain your answer.

5. Using your answers from above, finish the story.

CHAPTER 3
QUARANTINE ISLAND
(Roguish)

It's not like I didn't warn everyone. I warned them at every single turn; the rule book said one mistake, and we would end up on this island. I didn't really know what the island was called, but I knew we had been officially quarantined. So, for now, it was Quarantine Island.

You all may be reading this right now, waiting for me to spill my guts on this page, but I can honestly say, I don't know if I will. I don't know if I will because the ONLY way off this horrible island is if another group gets quarantined, then we can move back into the game to finish it.

I guess I did just let a little bit slip. So, I might as well tell you a bit more so that you don't pull your hair out trying to figure out what I'm talking about. I don't want to be 'that' person; the one that made you bald.

I could never forgive myself. My Uncle Wade was bald, and the sunburns he gets, oh man! I'll just say they're brutal for him and everyone around him.

So, here's your little slice of knowledge. I got suckered into a game...of sorts. I thought I was joining some sort of after school Dungeons and Dragons club, like a for-real club on Wednesday's. I love Dungeons and Dragons. I mean, who doesn't, right?

Last Wednesday, the bell rang, and I went into Mr. Foreman's classroom to meet up with everyone. The flyer said specifically, DO NOT BE LATE. I figured ten minutes after the meeting started would still be counted as on time.

I walked in and saw my five gaming partners walking through a doorway I never knew existed. I'd been in this classroom hundreds of times, but I'd never seen this door before.

It should have been my first clue to turn and walk away, but I didn't. The amazing neon blue light that was coming from the door overrode any desire I had to leave. I couldn't help myself; I inched closer to the door to see what it was.

My feet began shuffling faster as Kim waved at me to follow her. "Hurry up, Heath," she said.

I'd seen Kim play World of Warcraft, so needless to say, I'd follow her into any gaming situation. My eyes were beginning to burn a bit from the light, making me wish I had my sunglasses.

Stepping through the brightness and then back into normal light, I went. I ended up standing on a real-life game board. No joke, I was standing on the letter "S" in the phrase "Start Here." I remember saying, "Holy goat cheese!" Odd phrase, I know, but that's what I said.

The scenery was unreal. It was so vivid and bright, my eyes took a few seconds to adjust. Our mouths just hung open, and our eyes were as wide as softballs. We couldn't help it. It was so hard to explain what was happening right in front of my eyeballs. A glint of light, not too far from where we were standing, was begging for me to take a closer look.

I took about 15 steps off the board to take a look. Stacks and stacks of iridescent, pocket-sized books were all over the place. There were at least 10 stacks with as many as 80 books in each. These stacks should have been toppling over, but they weren't.

A sign, the same sign that was now glaring in my face, read:

TAKE A BOOK

HAVE A LOOK

FIND THE SOOK

I grabbed a book right from the middle of the stack. You can't blame me for wanting to see what would happen. All those books tumbling to the ground would have been worth the trip alone.

Unfortunately for you, I'm not going to tell you the rest. I've decided I've shared enough. If you want to know, you'll have to find your way here and GET ME OUT OF QUARANTINE ISLAND!

YOUR TURN:

1. Would you have followed Kim through the door?

2. Describe Quarantine Island.

3. What is a Sook?

4. Define the word roguish. Does this definition fit Heath? Explain your answer.

5. Using your answers from above, finish the story.

CHAPTER 4
SPELLING BEE
(Haughty)

Cassidy walked into school and immediately noticed the line of girls at the bathroom. This wasn't like the normal line that inevitably happened after 3rd period. Something was obviously going down. There was no way to see in, and she wouldn't dare cut in line.

Her curiosity didn't have to wait long before she saw what the commotion was all about. Pigtails and purple shirts all marched out at the same time and stopped right outside the bathroom door.

"Thank you all for waiting while we had our meeting," Sally said.

"Oh, no problem," murmured the majority of the girls now filing into the bathroom so they wouldn't be late.

A few girls asked Sally and the rest of her team for autographs, and of course, the school yearbook photographer started snapping shots as soon as Sally's good side was showing.

No one dreaded attention more than Cassidy, which was apparent by the way she pretended to read her new mermaid book while secretly peering over the top to get a glimpse at the new matching purple shirts.

The Spelling Bee Besties was the very team that Cassidy had wanted to be on since she learned of its existence. She'd been practicing for years. She could spell anything. Proving herself was a whole other story.

Longing to join the group was her favorite past time. She talked about the group as if she were part of them. Most of them didn't even know she existed.

Sally glanced over and interrupted Cassidy's stare. It was too late; the quick look down at her book wasn't quick enough. She could hear Sally walking towards her.

"What's your problem?" Sally asked.

"No problem," Cassidy said.

"Why are you stalking me?" Sally asked.

"I wouldn't call looking at you, stalking you," Cassidy responded.

"Call it whatever you want, but if you don't stop, you'll be sorry," Sally said.

"Already am," Cassidy said and turned and walked away.

Well, that was horrible and awkward all at the same time, Cassidy thought to herself. *Now I'll never get on the team.*

What made it worse was Cassidy's next class was English, and two rows over, yup…you guessed it, sat Sally.

The attendance bell rang, and as always, Sally strolled in with zero seconds to spare. She twirled her pigtail in Cassidy's direction and rolled her eyes.

"Class," Mrs. Wingate said. "We'll begin with our spelling challenges. Who would like to start?"

Sally's hand shot up like a rocket, and Mrs. Wingate hjumped back startled.

"OK, Sally," she said with a hand on her heart. "Spell chrysanthemum."

"Yes, Mrs. Wingate. Chrysanthemum. C-H-R-Y-S-A-T-H-E-M-U-M. Chrysanthemum."

Cassidy's eyes were popping outside of her head. Could she have mistaken what came from Sally's mouth? Were her ears not working correctly?

Mrs. Wingate looked down at the word on her notecard and said. "Sorry, that is incorrect."

The room gasped in unison. All eyes stared in pure disbelief. It was like they were glued to Sally, and no amount of fire department personnel would be able to unstick them.

"This is a difficult word. Who would like to take this challenge?" Mrs. Wingate said.

Cassidy's hand went halfway up and then jerked back down. *What is wrong with me? I'm already in hot water with Sally,* she thought to herself. *Do I really want to turn the flame up?*

"Cassidy, I saw your hand, although briefly. Chrysanthemum," Mrs. Wingate said.

All eyeballs ripped away from Sally and landed on Cassidy. The stares were so intense, every sweat bead could probably be seen before it fully escaped her pore. Her heartbeat could be heard throughout the school. She was sure of it.

If she gave the correct answer, Sally would make her sorry. Whatever that meant. If she gave the incorrect answer, she wouldn't be showing her true self.

She cleared her throat as both sides played ping pong in her mind.

"Yes, Mrs. Wingate. Chrysanthemum. C-H-..."

YOUR TURN:

1. What do you think Cassidy will do? Would you choose the same way?

2. Think about a club you are in or would like to be in. What type of behavior do they exude when everyone is together? Are individual behavior's different when they are not together? Why do you think that is?

3. Will Cassidy try to join the Spelling Bee Besties?

4. Define the word haughty. Does this word properly describe Sally? Explain your answer.

5. Using your answers from above, finish the story.

CHAPTER 5
FLYING SANDWICH
(Muddled)

My sisters Tiffany and DeLynn were off having fun without me. They were a bit older than me, and all the crazy stuff they were into, like hair appointments, glitter, and singing wasn't really my thing. No thanks. Goodbye.

I was playing ball with Ralph next door, and my stomach growled like I hadn't eaten in days. I split on Ralph and told him I'd be back over later.

As I reached my door, the wind began swirling, the clouds turned dark, and the temperature dropped 10 degrees. It was spring, and to be honest, I figured it was just another rainstorm blowing into town that would ruin all my fun.

Everything was fine until I sat down for lunch.

I made my sandwich like always, tossing white bread on my

plate, plopping on some ham, slapping on a slice of cheese, and finishing it off with a pickle on top. I positioned the top slice of bread perfectly to match the bottom slice and sat down to watch the clouds roll in.

My fingers felt shaky all of a sudden. *Why would I be trembling? Was it hunger?*

At that moment I realized, it wasn't my hands that were shaking. It was my sandwich! My cheese slowly began to wiggle its way out of my sandwich.

I dropped the sandwich on my plate like I just found a cockroach in it. Bread, cheese, meat, and the pickle were all just trembling like scared puppies in the pound.

A loud crack on the door made my head jerk to the living room. Now I really was the one trembling.

Looking back and forth between my sandwich and the door, I slowly slid my chair back and stood, putting my back to the wall. I couldn't decide which was more important to look at; the door or the sandwich.

CRACK!

The door shook, and a picture of my Mom fell off the living room wall. Glass shattered on the hardwood floor. My eyes bulged as my feet stepped closer to the door.

If my eyeballs had arms, they'd have been grabbing the handles of the cupboards, doing anything to stop my feet from going any further. Since that wasn't an option for them, they just grew bigger and bigger.

My heart was about to explode. I grabbed an umbrella from the stand next to the door, ready. Ready for what, I didn't know.

As I waited for whatever disgusting, evil thing was trying to break the door down to gain entry, I felt something behind me. I glanced back over my shoulder and saw that the sandwich was floating and trembling behind my right shoulder.

On a normal day, that would have made me run out the front door. Today, though, it wasn't the scariest thing happening at the moment. I had to concentrate on the biggest threat.

All of a sudden, the voices of my sisters came around the side of the house.

No! I thought. *Stay away. Can't you see whatever is pounding on the door?*

I raced to the doorknob without thinking, hoping to defeat this bully and save my sisters. It was too late, the door opened.

"What are you doing?" Tiffany asked.

My heart was the only thing that could be heard. My lips slowly parted, and I barely stuttered out, "I'm... um... I heard something?"

I quickly looked over my shoulder, hoping the sandwich would explain some things, but it was lifeless on the floor.

Perfectly still and in proper order right behind me in the middle of the living room.

"Matt, why is your sandwich on the floor?" DeLynn asked.

I scratched my head as my sisters walked past me and to their rooms.

Am I going crazy?

YOUR TURN:

1. What was on the other side of the door? And why was the sandwich shaking?

2. Why did it disappear when Tiffany and Amy came to the door?

3. Was this a real incident, or is Matt really losing his mind?

4. Define the word muddled. Does this word properly describe Matt's mind? Explain your answer.

5. Using your answers from above, finish the story.

CHAPTER 6
CURSIVE DROPOUT
(Meddlesome)

My parents, non-stop, commented on the fact that I wasn't learning cursive in school.

"How will you be able to read the constitution and know your rights if you can't read cursive? How will you sign for things? How can the school do this to our child?"

The list goes on and on. Trust me, you don't need to hear anymore. You really don't.

I knew enough cursive to read some of it, but it was tough, and I didn't care much about it. They worried way too much. It wasn't like my generation couldn't get through life without cursive. We had technology; we would be okay.

"I'm walking to the store to buy some gum. I'll be back!" I shouted from the front door.

"Be safe, Laura, and come right back," Mom shouted.

Ahhhh, fresh air, and no more talk about cursive. It was a beautiful day, and the birds never sounded so chipper. It was unreal how active they were. As I walked, I began to sense they were more agitated than chipper and social.

A murder of crows began to caw outrageously loud in the tree across the street. It was deafening and amazing all at the same time. I bet their voices could be heard for miles.

What has ruffled their feathers?

My hair began to rise a bit, like when my cousin used to hold me down and rub a balloon to my head. Static in the air was odd for sure this time of year.

I pulled out my money as I approached the store. I really didn't want to be in here longer than necessary. Bill, the owner, always tried to talk to me about his kids and how they never visited. His dentures clicked when he talked, and his breath always made my stomach flop because it smelled like dead fish.

The little bell rang as I opened the door. I made a beeline to the center aisle. Watermelon and grape were always my first two choices, but neither were in stock.

Dang. I guess regular bubble gum flavor will have to do.

"I'll take this," I said as I laid my gum on the counter and immediately set the exact amount of change on the counter. No dilly-dallying. No conversations. No stinky breath, I repeated in my head.

"Ah yes, original," Bill said. He picked up the pack and inspected it like he'd never seen gum before. "I remember when my kids were your age. Loved this stuff. They rarely visit me anymore. You know, I can barely get a phone call out of them."

"Sorry to hear that, Bill." My face turned green. Something came up in my throat, but I swallowed hard to keep it down.

"Not your problem," Bill said.

The register buttons beeped and beeped. It was an unusually long number of beeps before Bill looked at me. "We've had some new policy updates this week, with the new laws and such. I just need you to sign this receipt before you can have your gum," Bill said.

He handed me a pen and my receipt. A thin dotted line went from one end of the paper to the other.

"But I'm paying cash," I explained. "I don't have to sign if I'm paying cash."

"Actually, you do, if you want the gum," Bill said. "Last week, the government got to sticking their noses into the gum manufacturing business, and now they have a suspicion that it could be habit-forming. Can you believe that? Ha! Habit-forming."

"Okay, but why the signature?" I asked.

"They want to know who's buying all this gum so they can keep track of it all. That's all they said," Bill explained. He slightly raised both his hands up, shrugged his shoulders, then let his hands flop back down onto the counter.

"Are you serious?" I asked.

"Yes, don't you listen to the news?" Bill asked. "I had to spend all my petty cash to buy this new system, all for the government. I highly doubt they're going to compensate me in any way. You know, it was a financial burden on me, and they don't care. A lot like my kids. Not one of my children called me to ask how I was doing with this new law. They all know I had to get a new register."

I picked up the pen to sign because there was no way I was going to listen to any more talk about how his kids. My pen touched the line, and my fingers froze. What does he mean by a signature? I know how to print my name. It'll have to do.

My print was very legible, so there shouldn't be a problem for anyone to read it for any reason.

"Here," I said and handed the pen and receipt back.

"Well, thank you, Laura, but you printed your name on the signature line by accident. Your printed name goes up top. No, bother. I'll just put an arrow to the top line. Let's just put your signature below that," he said.

The receipt and pen were slid back to me. Bill eyed me as I hesitated.

"I guess I don't have a signature," I said. I wouldn't be able to hide the fact that I didn't know how to sign that receipt.

"You don't know how to sign your name?" Bill asked. "I find that hard to believe. It's just cursive."

Our eyes locked for a bit as I struggled to figure out how to continue this conversation. How could this be? I thought. It's absurd that I would have to use my signature. How am I supposed to know how to do this? Did I walk through a time warp where signatures are important? What is going on?

"I guess I won't get the gum then," I said.

"Your signature is an important part of your identity," Bill said. "It only takes a bit of practice."

"Yea, thanks," I said as I left the store empty-handed.

YOUR TURN:

1. Do you think cursive is important? Why or why not?

2. Do you think Bill is being honest? Why or why not.

3. Is this real, or did Laura enter a different dimension?

4. Define meddlesome. Do you think this is a proper word to describe Bill? Explain your answer.

5. Using your answers from above, finish the story.

CHAPTER 7
CHEERLEADING PRISON
(Contentious)

When I say that I was in cheerleading prison, people think I'm being cute. They smile and say something ridiculous like, "Oh, I bet it was just strict" or "It's good for you and your team, so you can be perfect at finals."

If being locked in a broom closet until I can get the perfect smile on demand is strict, then yeah, I guess strict would be accurate. For the rest of us, strict was an understatement. It didn't even come close.

I was totally excited to go before I knew what it actually entailed. I even helped my teammates onto the bus, and spying the matching bags made me energized.

"Thanks for helping with my bag, Tracy," Mable said.

"You're super welcome," I responded.

The bus arrived at our destination, and we couldn't believe the beautiful colors. My eyes couldn't keep up with the kaleidoscope before me. A dirt road made a perfect path through the flowers. Weeping willow trees lay several yards back from the flowers, making everything picture perfect.

The words, "This is amazing," were on repeat, recorded in everyone's voice. Unfortunately, I gave this prison a thumbs up on my *Sassy&Social* page before I even got to my dorm room.

BIG MISTAKE.

Our bus driver helped unload our bags, and we waved goodbye as he drove off.

After several moments, I felt something was off. I started counting all the gawking mouths and realized we were the only ones here. Just us, cheerleaders. The cheer squad in an unfamiliar place, on a dirt road. A very beautiful dirt road, but nonetheless, alone.

"Hey!" I shouted.

All glossy eyes stood at attention, waiting for the next words off my tongue.

"Does anyone know who is supposed to meet us here? Where are the adults? Are we supposed to wait for someone to escort us to the camp?" I asked.

Glossy eyes turned to blank stares, then to scared eyes. The chatter was getting louder and louder as everyone was trying to answer the questions. Hysterics were coming at any moment when a loud noise came from a ways down the lane.

"What was that?" Melissa asked. "Tracy, what do you think?"

"Um, I don't know," I said. "I think we need to get our baton's out until we see what's coming."

"You are always so paranoid, Tracy. I'm not sure why you're the captain. A good captain isn't paranoid," Melissa said.

"I'm getting out my baton. You all can do whatever you want," I said.

I heard 15 zippers open and rustling going on in bags. Everyone but Melissa waited for battle.

A rusty, dirty old pickup truck with the headlights cracked came up over the hill in the lane. It stopped about five yards in front of my group of heavy breathing, anxiety-driven, baton-wielding cheerleaders.

Bug guts and dried-up raindrops covered the windshield, and whoever was inside was not moving. It was the longest sixty seconds of my life.

The head behind the steering wheel cocked to one side as if studying us, then a big nose pointed towards the driver's side door, and it opened with a slow but steady SCREEEEEECH.

Melissa screamed a bit, and although I wanted to say, "Now who's paranoid, Melissa?" I didn't, because, to be honest, I was scared myself.

What in the world was coming out of that truck?

One black boot stomped to the ground and then the other. The bottom of a black skirt hung slightly below the door frame. Long, gangly fingers grabbed the top of the door, and with a big pull, she stood up from the driver's seat. Our necks bent backward, and our eyes popped.

"In...in... introduce us, Captain," Melissa stuttered and pushed me forward with her elbow.

YOUR TURN:

1. What is the first thing that Tracy says to the lady that got out of the pickup truck?

2. What types of punishment would the cheerleaders face at this cheer camp?

3. Do you think the cheerleaders were allowed to call their parents? Why or why not?

4. Define the word contentious. Do Melissa and Tracy have a contentious relationship? Explain your answer.

5. Using your answers from above, finish the story.

CHAPTER 8
CYPHER IN MY CEREAL
(Autocratic)

Crunch, crunch, crunch.

Adam had to eat his cereal fast because soggy cereal was a pet peeve he could not deal with. He could deal with many things like stepping on wet spots in his socks, having a runny nose and no Kleenex, and even an occasional wet willy. For some unknown reason, soggy cereal could turn Adam into a fuming hot-headed monster.

Crunch, crunch, crunch.

"Oooooouch!" Adam hollered. A small cylinder flew from his mouth and back into his cereal. His beady eyes got even smaller as he glared at his cereal.

"What's wrong, Honey Bunny?" Adam's mom yelled from her bedroom upstairs.

His head cocked to one side, listening intently. Beady eyes darted from his cereal bowl to the stairs.

Sounds that reminded Adam of a raging rhinoceros thundered through the upstairs hallway and then stampeded down the stairs. "Baby, what's wrong? What happened? Tell Mommy."

"I am 16 years old! Why do you continue to talk to me like that?" Adam shouted.

"Like what, Baby?" his mom asked. She leaned over and tried to pry his mouth open with her fingers to inspect.

"Get off! Go away!" Adam shouted. "I'm fine." His right hand cradled his right cheek. "I'm fine."

"Well, I suppose if your fine, my little bunny," she said and ran her fingers through his hair.

He slapped her hand away and said, "Would you stop?"

"Fine, I'll be upstairs watching my show," she said.

Rhino steps slowly faded down the hall, and beady little eyes stared at his bowl again.

Adam picked up his spoon and dug around in his cereal. Nothing came up from the now soggy mess. He let out an exaggerated sigh and then scowled.

Did I imagine it?

One more swirl of the spoon in his cereal and still nothing. Shaking his head, he got up to dump it down the drain. He poured slowly because he still couldn't believe that the hard, sharp chunk was part of his imagination. His tongue slipped over his tooth and sore gum. That didn't happen from his imagination.

There's no way I imagined it.

Using his left hand to hold the bowl, he started plucking out cereal with his other hand, one piece at a time. Soggy slippery, slimy cereal was squishing between his fingers, and his gag reflex started going into hyperdrive.

He set the bowl down and washed his hand thoroughly. He turned off the water and then turned it back on again. Washing them twice wouldn't hurt.

The metal colander sat in the cupboard where it had been his whole life. He'd never had a need to use it... until now. Now it sat in his sink and taking on the soggy, dripping mess that was too much for Adam to touch.

Clink!

Adam stopped pouring and set the bowl on the counter so fast the rest of the milk and soggy cereal spilled onto the counter without notice. A small metal cylinder lay at the bottom of the colander. Adam poked it as if a dragon might pop out.

"Don't be silly," Adam said out loud.

"About what?" his mom asked. She stood staring at him in the entryway.

Quickly turning and in a higher-pitched voice than normal, he responded. "Oh, oh ah, nothing."

The cylinder made a scraping sound as he snatched it up and pocketed it. "I'll be in my room."

"What about this mess," she said to his backside.

"Later," Adam responded.

His bed creaked as he slowly sat down. The cylinder was a precious treasure, and his eyes were transfixed on it. Fingers, way too big for it, twisted it this way and that. He tugged, pulled, and even chewed on it. Nothing would get it to open.

Although he wanted to throw it, he didn't. He placed it nicely on his desk in the bright sun so he could inspect it. It seemed to get very hot very quickly in the sun.

A small brown burn mark was forming on the desk from where the cylinder was sitting. Adam grabbed a shirt from his floor to use as an oven mitt when it opened, and a small scroll rolled out.

Adam's chest started to heave, and his fingers moved back and forth in delight as if he were tickling the air. Using his pointer finger from both hands, he slowly unraveled the soft brownish scroll and washed his eyes over the letters.

This wasn't fortune cookie type stuff. This was a cipher.

YOUR TURN:

1. What types of things would Adam really hate doing?

2. How did the cipher get into his cereal?

3. Create the cipher that is on Adam's paper.

4. Define the word autocratic. Do you think Adam's mom is autocratic? Explain your answer.

5. Using your answers from above, finish the story.

CHAPTER 9
RED BOX
(Strife)

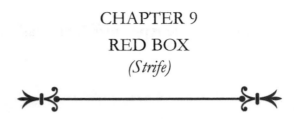

Here I was, right where my dad said I would be someday. He always lectured me that there would come a time when I would be in the middle of a big dilemma and have to decide whether to take the easy way or the hard way.

Some of the people involved in this whole debacle said there wasn't much to think about. They said, "It's obvious, you need to open the red box."

The problem with that was, that if they truly thought that was the right decision, then they would have opened the red box themselves. Once you hear what I have to say, you'll understand exactly. Or maybe you won't.

My story began with my girlfriend Sasha giving me this mysterious red box. The instructions were far from simple;

they read…

Dear Friend,

If you open this box, the secret is out. This secret could be good or bad, but you won't know until you see the contents. If the secret is good, our journey through life will be happy, full of love, and we will have many blessings in our future. If the secret is bad, my life will be ruined along with yours. If you can't make a decision, you must pass this box along, cross out my name at the end of this letter and add your own. But know this, every single person who has their name on this list will suffer the same fate as me and whoever opens it.

I'm sorry to put this burden on you.

Anonymous

~~Sarah~~

~~Joseph~~

~~Riley~~

~~Dawn~~

Sasha

Sasha received it from **Dawn**, who had received it from Riley. And now she'd passed it on to me because she couldn't possibly make this type of decision.

The problem was, I didn't want to make this decision either. My other dilemma was that I didn't want this burden to fall on anyone else. I felt pretty noble for saying that, but really, I wasn't being noble. I just **didn't** want anyone else to decide my fate.

I called a meeting with everyone on the list. Five friends sat in a circle with the red box between us. I wanted answers, and I wanted to get every inch of the story before I made a decision. I started with Sarah.

"Sarah, you were victim number one. Did you create this chain of events?" I asked harshly.

"Are you joking me, Tim! My whole world revolves around superstition. I'm Irish, remember. Heck no, I didn't start this! Whatever this is, could ruin my life and my families," Sarah said.

"How did you get it? Who gave it to you?" I asked.

"It was on my doorstep," Sarah said.

The distress in her eyes seemed real, but I wasn't going to make any hard decisions till later. "So, whoever started this really knows you," I said mostly to myself.

"It could have been anyone!" Sarah hissed.

"Why did you give it to Joseph?" I asked.

"I don't know. He was the first person I saw at school that day," Sarah said.

"Joseph, I see that some of the tape on one side is slightly lifted. I know for a fact, you can't handle having stickers, tape, or film on anything. Did you open the box already?" I said, pointing to the box.

I didn't wait for him to respond. "Tell me the truth," I said.

"Dude, I didn't do anything to that box, I swear," Joseph said.

"Let's just open the stupid box," Riley said. "We are all in this together. What are the chances that there's anything even in the box?"

"If that's what you really think, why did you pass this on and get Sasha and I involved?" I snapped.

Riley's eyes darted towards the floor.

"Does anyone have anything useful to say before I make my decision?" I asked.

"Well, I may know something," Dawn said. "I didn't think anything of it at first, but now I don't know. I don't know if it's even worth mentioning."

All eyes were on Dawn. Her breathing picked up, and her hands began to shake a little bit. Sasha reached over and held her hand.

"It's okay, Dawn. What is it?" Sasha asked.

YOUR TURN:

1. Does Tim open the box, pass it on, or do something else with the box?

2. What would you do?

3. Write down what is in the box, if anything.

4. Define the word strife. Do you think this word fits this group's situation at this moment? Explain your answer.

5. Using your answers from above, finish the story.

CHAPTER 10
DOOR IN A DOOR
(Psychosis)

Blackness was falling across the yard, and I knew it was only a matter of time before the porch light came on, and my mom's voice called out, "Stewart. Stewart, time to come in."

She always called, even though she could see me perfectly fine walking towards the back door. I don't know what it was, but she had to say it. It was like a tick now that she'd been doing it so long. A superstition is what she called it, but I didn't think so.

Darker and darker it became. My eyes squinted barely able to make out the silhouette of my hand, even when I wiggled my fingers. I turned towards my house and waited. But I heard nothing. I couldn't even see if she was on the back porch. Everything seemed to be silenced by an invisible blanket of thick air.

Odd.

I sat down on the swing and dangled my legs, intentionally not touching the ground.

Maybe she was waiting for me to come in on my own finally. Maybe she was going to let me show her how responsible I could be. She didn't have to call me, because I knew it was dark.

The longer I sat on my swing contemplating this turn of events, I came to the realization that the darker it got, the less likely my mom would trust me again because I wasn't moving towards the door.

I watched my shoes disappear like the sun. At that moment, I couldn't imagine a better place to be than my bedroom. The sheets were just washed and still had the springtime smell on them.

Laundry was all put away, and nothing was on the floor. The best feeling in the world was when my room was nice and tidy. I always slept better that way.

The cold metal in my hands grabbed my attention, and I once again looked around. A calming sensation turned into panic.

Why was I still out here in my backyard? Why wasn't I getting off the swing? Everything in my mind screamed to run for the house, but my body stayed in a relaxed state. I must be dreaming; that is the only logical reason. It must be a dream.

"I command you to get off the swing and head in!" I

shouted.

Nothing happened.

I couldn't wiggle my feet or my fingers. A picture of me inside a cage running back and forth, slamming into the bars to escape, was running like a movie behind my eyes.

I fell hard onto the mulch under my swing. The jarring stop sent all my limbs into forward motion. I jumped up and began to run. My breathing was having trouble keeping up with my feet. Cool air was hitting my hot face, and steam began to rise up then was left behind as I kept going.

The back door seemed miles away. My legs were aching, and my shoes were filling with sweat. The sidewalk was a welcome milestone in my furious attempt to get to my parents. *Where was my mother?* She should have come out yelling already.

Thick air started to saturate my mouth and lungs. The foul taste was something from a twisted movie, and fog set in. I couldn't see the door anymore, but it didn't matter. I was running in the right direction and would get to the door before something got me.

There was something in the fog. I could sense it. It was creeping up behind me ever so slowly even though I was running at full speed. It lived in the fog. It was the fog.

Reaching my hand out, I felt the doorknob, and with all my might and momentum, I turned the handle and pushed the door open. I fell on my face just inside the doorway. Or what should have been the doorway.

But I was shocked at the jagged feeling. It wasn't tile, like in the entryway of my house. My nose knew exactly where I was. The smell of dirt and mulch stormed through to my brain. My eyes finally focused on where I was and where 'it' was.

I lay under my swing face down. Pushing myself up with every ounce of energy I had, I then eyed the house. *What just happened?*

Sweat beaded on my forehead as the hairs on the back of my neck stood up. I turned slowly to face the back of the yard; a small waft of fog was creeping underneath the fence line.

YOUR TURN:

1. Describe this character: physically, mentally, and emotionally.

2. Determine why this character went through this event.

3. Describe the relationship this character has with his mom.

4. Define the word psychosis. Does this fit the situation? Explain your answer.

5. Using your answers from above, finish the story.

CHAPTER 11
SEARCH AND RESCUE
(Bemuse)

Rachael, where the heck are we going? Do you even know where we are going?" Stacy asked.

"Sort of," Rachael said.

The crinkled map was being studied intently. Rachael's fingers traced the map as if they were starving, and the different lines were feeding them. Back and forth, up and down, they traced the trails.

"Sort of isn't good enough," Stacy said. A tidal wave of tears instantly rolled down her cheeks. "What if we die out here?"

Leaves rustled more and more as the minutes ticked on. Clouds steadily crept in, getting more sinister-looking as they fell in line overhead. Rachael's fingers started getting cold, and soon she'd be seeing her breath.

"Got it!" Rachael shouted. "We're going to follow the stream back to the property line. Once we are here," she said, pointing at the map, "We will be just about 100 yards from my house."

"I think we need to stay put and wait for help," Stacy said.

"People die, waiting for help," Rachael said. "Let's go. Now.!

"Which way?" Stacy asked.

"Well, the river is going to be south of us. The sun is setting in the west, so this way," Rachael said. Her finger was shaking along with her voice. She picked up her bag and marched south.

Rachael kept her eyes south, only briefly looking back to see if Stacy was following. Any dissension would lead to conversation, more tears, and a delay their journey. A delay neither of them could afford if they wanted to survive.

Listening to Stacy's footsteps behind her gave her comfort, but a great sense of dread hung over what she felt was right.

What if she was wrong?

"Rachael wait, I'm tired. Are you sure we don't have any more food?" Stacy asked. "Or water?"

"Here, take this cough drop," Rachael said. She pulled a white wrapper out of her pocket as she walked. Her pace never changed as she meticulously tromped through the foliage and weaved between the trees. Stacy picked up the pace to snatch it out of her hands.

Suddenly the girls stopped, and smiles traveled from ear to ear. The sound of water rushing along a riverbed played sweet music, washing their fear downriver.

"Yes!" Stacy shouted. "You are amazing, Rachael. How did you know to do this?"

"We're not home yet. Let's keep walking," Rachael replied. Her face could not hide her excitement, although her mouth refused to speak words of victory.

Simultaneously they picked up the pace. Their breathing began to get heavier as they fought through some of the brush.

"Rachael, how do you know all of this survival stuff?" Stacy asked again.

"My mom. She's a fanatic about making sure I can find my way back home. She's always wanted me to feel comfortable surviving in the woods. Ever since I was a baby," Rachael sighed.

"Well, it sure as heck paid off," Stacy said.

"Yea, it did, hopefully," Rachael said. "We don't celebrate or claim victory until we're inside my house, okay? Don't jinx it by dancing just yet."

"Totally agree, girl," Stacy said. "Why is your mom all crazy about you being able to live in the woods? It's kind of weird, don't you think?"

"When my mom was little, her brother died from exposure. He got lost in the woods, and they couldn't find him. She built the rest of her life around finding people," Rachael said. Tears welled up and trickled down.

"That's heavy, I'm sorry," Stacy said.

"Don't be. It's fine," Rachael replied.

"We will get out of this. I'm not dancing, so no jinxes here, but we will be okay," Stacy said and gently wiped away Rachael's tears.

"I just don't want my mom to worry," Rachael said. "She would be devastated if she knew we were out here. She'd be even more pissed if she knew why we came out here. I don't want her to think I'm irresponsible."

Their feet began to ache as the continued their walk, but the quick pace was maintained.

"You are the most responsible person I know. I would like to add, the only one that I know who could get us home. That's pretty dang responsible. If your mom finds out, she will be happy you saved us," Stacy said trying her best to reassure her friend.

"Thank you for saying that," Rachael said.

YOUR TURN:

1. What were Stacy and Rachael doing out in the woods?

2. Have you ever been lost? How did that feel?

3. Would you have stayed and waited for help?

4. Define the word bemuse. Does this word fit with Rachael and/or Stacy? Explain your answer.

5. Using your answers from above, finish the story.

CHAPTER 12
YOUR WORD
(Clandestine)

"You gave me your word," Cedric said. "We swore to never speak of the drawings or how we found them."

"I know, and I'm sorry," Penelope responded apologetically.

Tears trickled down her cheeks. She couldn't wipe them away fast enough. Finally, using two hands, she covered her face.

"Here," Cedric said, handing her a tissue.

Feelings of betrayal flooded his mind, and as much as he wanted to cry with her, he couldn't. The anger was just beginning to build. The act of disloyalty was too great to cry for. His trust in her was once very great, but now, all of that was all gone.

"Thank you," she said. "I didn't want to do it. I had to. They were going to find out about the Clandestine Project if I didn't tell them."

"I just finished destroying the drawings to make sure we couldn't be connected to them. So we don't need to worry about that. But you could have told them a lot of other things as well." Cedric replied.

"No, I couldn't have. I didn't. Please believe me," Penelope begged.

"Why would I believe you now?" he challenged.

Her hand reached out towards his arm, but Cedric moved backward and walked around the couch, keeping some distance between them.

"They knew about the drawings already. I don't know how!" Penelope insisted. "They were trying to figure out how we got them."

"What? Not possible," Cedric replied. He closed the gap between them. "What exactly was said, Penelope?" he demanded.

Tears spilled over her lower eyelids again as she used the tissue, which was already at its max capacity for tears. Cedric handed her another tissue.

"They said that they found your drawings on a USB drive that was left in your work shirt, in your locker. They described the drawings to a 'T'. They have to have it somehow, or they wouldn't have been able to give such great detail," Penelope said.

"That's not possible," Cedric said.

"Clearly it is," Penelope barked. The tears stopped, and her face turned red. "They found my name on that USB drive, Cedric. Why was my name on it?"

"Again, not possible," Cedric said. His eyes glazed over, thinking about all the times that USB drive had been used.

Had he forgotten to erase old files with their names on them?

Clandestine Project started as a way to get information so they could send anonymous letters to the newspaper about things that were not right in the community. Sometimes they wrote about good events that weren't being recognized in the community, but it was mostly back-alley not so positive stuff.

All that back-alley stuff gave way to some pretty ugly things, and they were found out by the local police after theyd' witnessed some crazy stuff. They swore off the project but never really stopped.

"The Crater brothers couldn't have gotten all of that information from the USB, Penelope," Cedric said. "They must have something else."

Piles of paper and gadgets were flying out of a box that Cedric pulled from his closet. A USB drive dangled in front of Penelope's face.

"This is the USB drive. The only one that had files on it," Cedric said.

"Pop it in. I want to see exactly what's on this one," Penelope said.

Cedric looked at her red eyes for a long time before agreeing. His happy heart danced when he found it, but it began to sink, thinking about the consequences if this was not the right USB.

Am I the one that let her down? The one that made the mistake. Should I be the one begging forgiveness?

"I told the Crater brothers about our involvement with Mr. and Mrs. Bandings and that we found the drawings in their basement." Penelope explained. "I made it seem like that was the only thing we knew. I figured that was way less incriminating than all the Clandestine Project stuff. Plus, the Bandings moved out of the country, so the chances of them tracking them down are slim."

Now that her tears were done flowing. She threw the tissues away.

YOUR TURN:

1. What were the drawings of?

2. Will Cedric and Penelope mend their relationship?

3. What is on the USB drive?

4. Define the word clandestine? Does the project name fit what they were doing? Explain your answer.

5. Using your answers from above, finish the story.

CHAPTER 13
LUCY ENTER
(Abhorrent)

"You in the back, can you hear me? Yes, you. Okay good. I want everyone to laugh. Everyone should be having their mouths open wide and having a good laugh. Are you listening? You hear my words? Let's laugh, people. Laugh like your actors, for goodness sakes!" Mr. Schneider yelled.

His hands waved as he talked, and even when his mouth shut, many times, they were still waving. His squatty stature didn't hinder his ability to jet across the stage, shouting and waving.

"If you can create tears from laughing, let's do that. Who can do that? No one? Okay. Who's going to try?" Mr. Schneider's hands were in the air and then fell to his hips. "You should all be raising your hands right now. Everyone needs to try during this next scene."

"Take it from the top. Lucy enters from the left, and go!" Mr. Schneider yelled.

His hands stayed around his mouth as his eyes watched the curtains on the left. He leaned forward a bit, resting his body against the table in front of him. Papers were strewn around like they were ready to protect the table from a painting project.

Red curtains that were stained with make-up, grime, and dirt from the years of theater productions remained still. The stage was like a barren land. No one moved, no one dared.

"Lucy, enter left, from the top, GO!" Mr. Schneider yelled again. His portly arms must have gotten tired because they lay to his side, surrendering.

"Paul, go get her," Mr. Schneider yelled. He pulled his arms out of their resting position and waved them around as if conducting a symphony.

"Does she not know her left from her right? Does anyone know? If not, this could be an issue. I'm just saying." Mr. Schneider said as he pushed his chair to the side and walked towards the stage.

The finish on the wood was worn out and caused rough spots that all the actors knew to avoid when performing. It came chest high to Mr. Schneider, so he did what he could to see over; stretching his neck out like a chicken on a chopping block to see to the left side.

"Paul!" he yelled.

Silence was the response. Eyes went from each other to the backstage area on both sides.

"What in the world is going on?" Mr. Schneider said mostly to himself.

He let out a long and exaggerated sigh. His eyes rolled as far over as possible without rolling right out of his head. Big clumsy feet shuffled to the stairs on the left. The railing was sturdy and never made a peep as it helped heave Mr. Schneider to the stage.

Standing just outside the left entrance, he looked around, waiting for something to jump out at him. Nothing. All was quiet and empty.

Slowly, wary now, he continued on. One foot in front of the other, much quieter than his shuffle, led him behind the curtain to the back. Bewildered by what he saw, his mouth dropped open, but no words came out.

Lights flickered, and a green vortex lay 10 feet from his stubby nose. Voices came from the swirling green light. Voices he recognized. Two of those muffled voices made their way to Mr. Schneider's ears. "Help us. Help us," they cried.

Every muscle in his body went stiff, and Mr. Schneider froze, searching for explanations.

YOUR TURN:

1. Describe how the actors probably felt about Mr. Schneider.

2. If you were Paul and saw this, what would you have done?

3. What will Mr. Schneider do?

4. Define the word abhorrent? Does this word fit Mr. Schneider? Explain your answer.

5. Using your answers from above, finish the story.

CHAPTER 14
BALL TIME
(Thwarted)

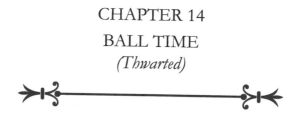

The basketball court was completely empty, but that didn't bother me. I enjoyed being able to just shoot hoops by myself. It gave me a break from the hustle of the game. Shooting by myself gave me time to visualize where I wanted to be and what type of player I would become.

My mom hired a personal basketball coach for me because she wanted me to go pro. He talked to me about visualization and how to make my thoughts focus at home in my head as much as they were on the court.

Coach Randy cost a lot, but my mom didn't care. She picked up extra shifts for six months to get him. All those long hours for her, I couldn't let them go to waste. My mom was counting on me to help our family.

I stepped up to the free throw line. I placed my right foot slightly ahead of my left, squared up to the basket, and took the shot. Nothing but net.

Chasing the ball then dribbling to the three-point line, I couldn't help but pretend I was in the last few seconds of a game and just let it fly. The ball nicked the rim and then sank in. *Three points!* My thoughts were racing around the fame and fortune I would have when I made it big.

Thirty more shots with only one miss, that was a victory for me. Coach Randy said to always strive for 100 percent of my shots, which was a no brainer, but he also said if I miss, not to let it bother me. I already had what it takes inside, so missing a shot wasn't the end of the world. It was just a matter of more practice.

Sweat was pouring down my face when I palmed the ball and turned to walk home. The exit was on the other side of the court. A slight pain made itself known around my shin. I stopped and rubbed my right leg.

Probably just my shoes being worn out. I'd just have to get new ones.

Several more steps and the pain got worse. I hopped on my left foot to the bleachers and sat down. The pain vanished as long as I didn't stand on it.

I kept thinking to myself, *How could I have broken my leg? What is going on? Then after a few minutes, I thought, How am I going to get home?*

I waited for about 20 minutes, just chilling on the bleachers letting my leg rest, before I decided to try again. Fear of pain made me hesitate, but I couldn't sit here all day. I had to get back home or my mom would worry.

I slowly lowered my right foot to the ground. I carefully applied my weight on it and began to walk. With each step, the pain began to slowly increase. I wouldn't be able to make it home before needing to rest again.

"Luke!" I heard from behind me. Keeping all my weight on my left leg, I swung around and saw Kevin riding his bike towards me.

"Dude!" I yelled back. "Give me a ride home."

"Why? What's wrong with you?" Kevin asked without even waiting for a response.

"I don't know. My leg hurts like crazy. Hurts to walk," I said.

"If you can't walk, you won't be able to stand on my pegs evenly," he said. "That's not going to work."

"True. This sucks," I said.

"What happened?" Kevin asked, this time giving me time to respond.

"My leg feels like it's on fire when I step down," I said.

"Well, you're lucky. I'm smart. Here, sit on my bike," Kevin said.

"I can't use the pedals," I said.

"Sit down on the seat, use your good leg to push off, keep your other leg resting on the pedal. It'll take a while to get to your place, but it's better than hopping the whole way," Kevin explained.

"You're a genius," I said.

"I know," Kevin responded.

YOUR TURN:

1. Who do you think wants Luke to go pro more, his mom, or himself?

2. Make a list of all the possible ailments that could be making Luke's leg hurt.

3. Choose an ailment and describe how that would affect his ability to play basketball in the present and future.

4. Define the word thwarted? Does this word fit in the story? Explain your answer.

5. Using your answers from above, finish the story.

CHAPTER 15
MISSING
(Anomalous)

Every morning is the same at my house. Completely the same. Every single morning, I go down the stairs, my mom brings me cereal, and then I watch some T.V. until I need to get ready for school.

This morning was like any other. I shuffled down the stairs like always. Scratching the back of my head and then moving the hair out of my eyes, I began to feel like something was off. It was unusually quiet. The word unusual was the keyword here.

The hairs on the back of my neck stood up when I saw the kitchen. My mouth popped open like a hungry hippo. Coffee was draining from the coffee maker onto the warmer, then spilling over the edge to the counter and splashing onto the floor. I grabbed the pot that was in the sink and put it in its place to catch what little coffee was left.

All the dishes from the dishwasher and cabinets were stacked as high as possible on the countertops. Everything was teetering, just waiting for a passerby to make a quick movement to send it toppling over.

My bowl of cereal sat on the table, but it looked a bit funny. On further inspection, it wasn't cereal that was soaking up milk in my bowl. It was dog food.

As my heart began pumping in rapid succession, my eyes noticed a note.

What the heck is going on? I thought as I grabbed the note from the refrigerator.

Terry,

Breakfast on table. Enjoy.

Love,

Parents

"What?" I shouted. "This makes no sense!"

I jumped and dropped the letter when I heard the trash can collide with the cement. *That was so loud.* I turned slowly towards the back door and saw an inch worth of the backyard peeking through the gap in the door. *Was it open when I walked into the kitchen?*

Crash!

My feet lifted off the floor for a brief moment. I lunged to the door and shut it tight. The deadbolt was the first turn. The lock on the handle was the second.

"Hi," came a voice behind me.

"Ahhhh!" I yelled.

There was no way I was okay. *I'm going crazy. How could this happen? My doctor said I was fine at my physical.* My brain continued to run through these thoughts as the fuzzy little monster came closer.

"Hi," it said again.

Frozen in place, all I could do was blink. I blinked over and over again as if my eyes were trying to wipe away this creature like wiper blades in the rain.

"Okay?" it asked.

My head involuntarily tilted to one side. "No," I responded. I became out of breath all of a sudden. The mere act of saying 'No' was just too much for my lungs. They were exuding too much energy.

"Sorry to you," it said.

"Where's my mom?" I asked, winded.

"Safe. Safe. Fun," it said.

YOUR TURN:

1. Describe in detail what this creature looks like.

2. Should Terry feel threatened? Why or why not?

3. Where are the parents?

4. Define the word anomalous. Does this word fit with what is going on? Explain your answer.

5. Using your answers from above, finish the story.

CHAPTER 16
MAGIC FLOWERS
(Surreptitious)

The flowers bloomed a bit earlier at our house. Our neighbors always commented on how bizarre it was. We would have a full flower garden bursting with life as theirs were just popping up out of the soil.

I didn't really understand it. Anytime I would ask Mom about it, her response was always, "It's the love we give them. The rest we'll talk about when you're older."

Who had secrets about flower gardens? Apparently, my family. We had a lot of secrets when it came to our plants.

My parents were plant people to the max. My mom was just a gardener before she and my dad started working together. My dad was a scientist, who worked specifically with plants.

Some nights they would be locked in debate about their

most current experiment till long after I went to bed. One time, my mom even tried to sway my dad as she said grace at the dinner table. That didn't go over well.

Nothing they said ever gave me a clue as to what was behind the locked door in the basement, a.k.a. their work area. One time I tried to break in, and a loud alarm went off. Some men in black suits showed up at the house, and I had to sit next to one that looked like he was a pro wrestler until my parents got home.

That was a bad day for me. Except it did give me a little insight, so it wasn't a complete loss. With as few words as possible, my parents explained that they worked for a top-secret plant company.

That same night while I was in my room reading, I heard a loud boom. The basement door slammed against the wall, footsteps stomped quickly up the basement stairs, and the front door crashed open. All the while, my mom was screaming, "Throw it in the front yard. Stop touching it. Hurry!"

After that night, the flowers stayed in bloom through the middle of winter. We were talked about throughout the neighborhood, and when all the garden and plant magazines started calling for interviews, my parents put up a fence.

Even with the fence, our nosey neighbor Sandy would come right into the yard with a plate of cookies and about three friends in tow to say Happy or Merry and then fill in the holiday. Every holiday, even ones nobody ever really celebrated, we got cookies while her friends were looking around in awe.

We all knew it was a ruse to see our garden. It irked my parents terribly, but those cookies were so good. I made sure to tell her that I couldn't wait to see her again.

Four nights ago, my mom told me, "Deanna, your dad and I have to go on a trip for work. We will be leaving in the morning."

"That's not much notice," I said.

"No, but something has come up, and we were called in. Aunt Dixie is coming over to watch you, but she won't get here till tomorrow. You'll have to stay here just one night by yourself, okay," Mom said.

She grabbed me and gave me a big hug. Tears were hitting the top of my head.

I pushed myself away from her. "Why are you crying? How long will you be gone?" I asked.

"Because I don't want to leave you by yourself and we will only be gone five days," Mom answered.

We spent most of that night in my parents' room as they packed, and we laughed more than we ever had. Odd, that they were so focused on talking about memories of our family outings and telling me how much they loved me. I sure enjoyed it, though.

The next morning, things happened so fast. My mom got me up and made me breakfast. Before I was even finished, a loud bang came from the front door.

"That's our ride," Dad said. He gave me a big hug. You remember all the instructions I gave you?"

"Yes," I said.

"Good, I love you, pumpkin. We will be back before you know it," Dad said with a quiver in his voice. He kissed my forehead and walked away.

"Dad?" I had so many questions but he had already gone out the door.

"Bye, honey. I love you. Remember about your chores and remember to take a shower and brush your teeth every day," Mom said.

"I know," I said.

"Aunt Dixie will be here tomorrow morning. My phone will always be on. Lock up the whole house. I'd rather you not go outside until Dixie's here," Mom said.

"Okay," I said. My eyes automatically rolled; I couldn't help it.

My mom was locking the door from the outside before I could even lean over to look out the window and wave.

Thirty seconds later, they were outside the fence and gone.

YOUR TURN:

1. What type of plant projects do Deanna's parents work on?

2. Where did the parents go, and why?

3. Did Aunt Dixie show up?

4. Define the word surreptitious. Does this word fit with the story? Explain your answer.

5. Using your answers from above, finish the story.

CHAPTER 17
THREE DOORS
(Captive)

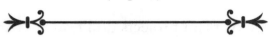

I'm standing in front of three doors. Door number 1 says *Unicorn*, door number 2 says *Dragon*, and door number 3 says *Chocolate*.

I would love to say this is a dream, but it's not. I actually have no idea what this is or how I got here. But, here is what I do remember…

I woke to my little brother screaming because he wanted more sugar on his cereal. My mom seemed more tired than normal. She had deep, dark circles under her eyes, but she was talking back to him in a calm voice like always.

And like always, it wasn't working, so my dad poured a pinch more sugar in his bowl, and he stopped screaming. My mom gave my dad 'the look,' and he left the kitchen.

So, it was going to be one of those days, I thought. I couldn't handle this for the third day in a row.

The whole family seemed off and at its wit's end. There was a thickness in the air, and I couldn't tell what it was. This weird air was seeping into everyone's emotions and messing with them.

Calling my friends and having them meet me at the mall seemed like a great plan. Or, at least a great escape from whatever was infecting my family. Three friends agreed, so I took a shower, hopped on my bike, and took off.

We always met at the gothic store first. None of us were goth, but it was fun to look and try on all the bracelets and read the stickers. The music was crazy loud, and I remember thinking it was louder than usual, and the owner was zoned out.

Not the kind of zoned out from not having enough sleep, but a zoned out from life in general. It was strange. Everyone ignored it, and we moved on to the next store.

Wandering in and out of the shops and laughing was great. We weren't being told to calm down at all, which was a bit weird.

Usually, we would see a mall cop here and there. One who would, at the very least, give us the 'you better behave and watch yourself' look. Store owners would 'mean mug' us, and other shoppers would shake their heads.

It wasn't like we were bad kids. We were just a bit rowdy.

We were being rambunctious next to the skater shop, and the next thing I remember was we were walking calmly down the sidewalk towards the food court. I was so hungry, yet I couldn't go any faster. It was like I was in a lazy river, and my legs were the water, going in slow motion.

My thoughts were filled with food, and I was happy and content with thinking about the corndog, fries, and soda I was going to be stuffing my face within just a few minutes. I turned to look at my friends, Mike, Collin, and Sam. They seemed to be in a daze with big smiles on their faces.

"Hey!" I said in a calm voice.

"Yeah?" Sam said.

"Do you guys feel weird?" I asked.

"No. I feel good, "Mike said, "And happy."

"Me too," Collin agreed. "How do you feel, Caden?"

"I'm great, actually. I think something is wrong, though. I feel like we are not our normal selves," I said. I was trying to protest, but my happy, corndog thoughts wouldn't let me get upset.

"Corndogs!" I said in a giddy voice.

Grabbing our food and sitting down, we were all just quiet. My brain kept telling me to stop, or run, or grab my friends and get out, but I couldn't. My brain refused to send the signal out to my legs to run. My brain was being run by someone else.

A picture of a mad scientist popped into my head. I could imagine him using my gaming controller to control my moves and thoughts. *Was that even possible?*

My eyes began to water, and the biggest yawn I've ever had escaped my mouth. Keeping my eyes open was turning into the most difficult thing ever.

The next time my eyes opened, I was here. Standing in front of these three doors.

YOUR TURN:

1. Why is everyone acting the way they are acting?

2. How did Sam get to the doors?

3. What is behind the doors?

4. Define the word captive. Does that word fit with this story? Explain your answer.

5. Using your answers from above, finish the story.

CHAPTER 18
SORRY ABOUT YOUR DOG
(Supernatural)

Ring. Ring. Ring. Ring. Ring.

"Hello, Mr. Hauge?" I asked.

"Yes, who is this?" Mr. Hauge asked.

"This is Anthony. I live down the street," I said.

"Okay," he responded.

"Well, ah, sir. Ah, I have to tell you something that I did," I said.

"Go on, boy, I don't have all day. What is it?" he asked.

"I was trying to jump your fence because it's two inches higher than normal, and I'm practicing my hurdles," I explained.

"Hmmm," Mr. Hauge said.

"Yea," I said and paused. "Well, I didn't realize you had a dog."

"Excuse me?" Mr. Hauge asked.

"I'm really sorry. I only noticed it when I landed," I explained.

"My dog?" Mr. Hauge asked.

"Yes," I responded. "Anyway, it was barking at me, so I ran out the front gate, and before I could shut it, he ran down the street. I tried to run after him, but he just disappeared somewhere."

"Disappeared," Mr. Hauge repeated. A long steady breath escaped through his whistling nose.

"I'm very sorry," I said.

"No need to be sorry, boy. I don't own that dog," he replied.

"You don't? Are you watching it for a friend?" I asked.

"No, I don't watch it. It watches me," he said.

"Um, okay," I said. This was not at all how I expected the conversation to go.

"I was young like you once, and I let that same dog out of a neighbor's yard. It followed me home and has watched me every day since," Mr. Hauge said.

77

"I don't think it's possible to have a dog live that long," I said. I gave a sheepish smile even though I knew darn well that he couldn't see me.

"I didn't think so either. I'm sorry. I don't know what that animal is, but I can assure you, it's not a dog. I'm sorry, son," he said.

"Sorry?" I asked.

The line went dead. "Hello?" I called into the receiver. I yelled 'hello' a few more times before I looked at the screen on my phone and realized he had hung up.

WOOF!

I stared at the front window for a good 30 seconds before my brain caught up with what I was seeing. Without realizing it, I was up and standing at the window. Panting and whimpers could be heard. Less than an inch of glass separated me from whatever that was.

YOUR TURN:

1. Describe what this dog looks like.

2. Does this dog stay with Anthony?

3. Does Anthony contact Mr. Hauge again?

4. Define the word supernatural. Does this word fit with this story? Explain your answer.

5. Using your answers from above, finish the story.

CHAPTER 19
MARCHING BAND
(Dissident)

"Did you see the new uniforms?" Desirae asked.

"No," said Dean. "Are they cool?"

"No. Not at all," Desirae said. A long sigh escaped her mouth as she slumped over onto her book. The desk seemed to be the only thing holding her up.

"Come on. They can't be that bad," Dean said.

"Just wait, you'll see. I can't believe we have to start marching in them this next competition. That's only two days away. I won't get used to this uniform in two days," Desirae said.

"What are you talking about, getting used to it?" Dean asked. "It's a uniform."

The bell rang, and Desirae got up. "You'll see."

Dean sat a bit, trying to wrap his brain around what could be so horrible. He didn't have to wait long. Marching band was his next class.

Walking down L hall, a rubbery smell, like tires, began to tickle his nose. He had to plug his nose and then rub the sides to squeeze any existing smell out of his nostrils.

Desirae walked out of the classroom, bumped Dean's shoulder, and yelled. "I'm going to quit. Is it too late to quit?"

The instrument locker area was silent.

Peaking around the corner, Dean saw a ginormous tire was sitting against the back wall, next to the drums section.

"Wow," Dean said. His eyes were wide and his jaw dropped. *What does a tire have to do with band?* The question kept twirling around in his head like the color guard flags.

A few more steps and Dean's eyes connected with the new uniforms. Some of the students were wearing them, trying to smile, but they couldn't hide the 'help I'm trapped in a junkyard suit' look.

Three girls from the flute section were just crying in the corner, and Tonia from the saxophone section sat completely blank-faced. A little white, but in a completely different world like she was trying to block out the travesty of it all.

"See!" Desirae wailed.

You could hear a pin drop as soggy eyes, glazed over eyes, and panicky eyes turned to silently beg Dean and Desirae to do something.

"Oh, good!" Mrs. Joslin yelled from behind her desk. "Come here, Dean. Let's get you fitted!"

Eyes got bigger, and heads began to slowly shake from side to side. Desirae shuttered.

"If you don't say something, we are toast with this uniform," Desirae whispered fervently. Her hand grabbed his forearm, and she gave a slight squeeze. "She listens to you."

Heads in the sea of junkyard debris quickly nodded, causing some clashing of instruments against the suits.

"Dean, let's go," Mrs. Joslin shouted again.

As Dean turned to go into Mrs. Joslin's office, he could hear people taking a deep breath and not letting it out.

"Hey, Mrs. Joslin," Dean said as he slowly walked through the door frame. "So, why the new suits? What was the inspiration?"

"You know art and magnificence when you see it. I can tell. I love talking about inspiration," Mrs. Joslin said. "Have a seat."

A notepad lay on top of a mess of music sheets and 'How To' books. Mrs. Joslin had been reading her newest edition of How to Make a World Class Marching Band.

"I've never known anyone to care as much about marching band as you," Dean said.

"Let me get your suit out of the closet so you can go try it on," Mrs. Joslin said. "My other passion is recycling. I love it, and now I have decided to combine the two."

YOUR TURN:

1. Describe the marching band uniform.

2. Does Dean talk Mrs. Joslin out of wearing the uniform?

3. Describe the comments they would get during the competition.

4. Define the word dissident. Does that word fit with the story? Explain your answer.

5. Using your answers from above, finish the story.

CHAPTER 20
Class President
(Arrogant)

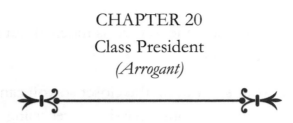

Being Class President was going to be the highlight of my school career. Voting was held last night after our speeches, and the announcement of the winner was going to happen in homeroom today. I didn't want to boast too much to my friends, but I did give quite a few nods of acceptance this morning.

There were so many people patting my back and giving me high five's, I knew I had it in the bag. I'd been handing out buttons for over a month. I went to all the different clubs and events to make sure everyone was super familiar with my face.

My plan was to make sure people knew I cared. That's what a president does. They make it a point to know who all their people are, what they like and don't like. Interjecting myself into everyone's business made sure I didn't miss anything.

I got a lot of questions like, "Why do you need to know?" and "Why do you care?" I answered all of them with, "Because I care about my people, of course."

Reading their faces was sometimes a bit hard, but overall, I'm sure they appreciated my attention and concern with their every waking move. I mean, who wouldn't want their class president to be involved. Some people actually went out of their way to rub elbows with their new president.

Soon, I'm sure I'd have to be turning people away at the lunch table so I could concentrate on my plans. Plans like no more library fines or hallway passes. We were all basically adults, and having to have a hallway pass was ridiculous.

Homeroom erupted in smiles as I walked in. My cheeks turned red at the adulation, but that was something I would have to get used to. I bowed and took my seat.

Dylan walked up behind me and slapped my shoulder. "Hey Doug, I can't wait for hallway passes to go away," he said.

"Same here, thanks for your vote," I said and stuck out my hand.

"I didn't vote for you. I'm hearing lots of people did, though. You probably got it," Dylan said.

"You didn't vote for me? Why not?" I asked.

"Well, a lot of reasons," Dylan said. His mouth opened to continue speaking, and the bell rang. He snapped his mouth shut and walked over to his desk, all casual-like. Like he hadn't just given me a devastating blow to my ego.

At least he said I was going to win, sort of. He's probably that one fluke of a friend that has weird views on everything in life.

The announcements began, and my thoughts were racing.

Had I been giving everyone the inconspicuous nod of acceptance when I didn't even win? Were people laughing as they slapped my back because they knew I had no chance, and now I'm the fool?

Now that I was looking back at my morning, there were some people who avoided eye contact, I'm sure of it.

Oh no, I lost. I know I did.

"I will now announce the next Class President," a shrill voice echoed through the loudspeaker.

YOUR TURN:

1. Think about a time when you doubted yourself. Write out what happened, including the end result.

2. Do you think people were really avoiding eye contact with Doug or was it part of his imagination due to self-doubt?

3. Do you think Doug is the new Class President?

4. Define the word arrogant. Does arrogance fit Doug's behavior in this story? Explain your answer.

5. Using your answers from above, finish the story.

CHAPTER 21
THE OTHER SIDE
(Boondoggle)

"Kenny, we have to go back. Open it up!" Pat yelled.

"We can't! I've said it 100 times. We can't go back through the doorway. It's too dangerous," Kenny said.

"What is wrong with you! Mary is still stuck out there. We can't just leave her," Pat pleaded.

"Mary chose to leave our group when we were headed back. Have you forgotten that Everett is so shaken up he can't even talk right now?" Kenny asked.

"Of course not," Pat said. Her voice was shallow as her eyes met Everett's. Her cheeks drained of color as she watched him shake uncontrollably.

Kenny got up and rubbed Pat's arm. "No one wants to

abandon Mary, but she left on her own accord. She instructed us to keep going and not wait for her. We need to honor her request."

Crystal stood up for the first time since everyone poured back through the doorway. "Something was by the doorway, on the other side," she said, pointing. "I saw something. It was all black. It grabbed Everett and injected something into his skin."

Kenny and Pat's eyes widened at Crystal's account of what happened. They both silently turned to study Everett. He hadn't said a word since they got back.

Everett's skin was a pasty white. The shaking seemed to be getting better with every minute, but his behavior was not.

"Look at all his goosebumps. I'll get him a blanket," Crystal said.

"Wait a minute," Pat said. She inched closer and watched Everett's skin. "I don't think those are goosebumps. They keep popping up and then going down, then moving. It looks like something with scaly skin is moving underneath his skin."

In unison, they all took a few steps back. Their breathing was light, and their movement slow and intentional, as if they were trying to not wake a rabid bear.

Everett's breathing became more rapid, and his eyes began to flutter under his closed eyelids. His fingers began to twitch, and the tips were turning black. Sweat streamed down his forehead, darkening the color of his shirt from the moisture.

Kenny, Pat, and Crystal tiptoed to each other, huddling by the doorway. Their eyes were darting back and forth between each other, their heads shaking and shoulders shrugging as their fingers did all the work, giving instructions on what they should do.

The doorway lay only feet from the trio, and it began to crackle. All movement ceased, even Everett's.

"What do we do?" Pat asked.

"We can't open the door. That thing is on the other side," Crystal said.

"We can't keep it shut because we may have to get whatever is in Everett out and back to the other side," Kenny said.

"What if there are more of them, and Mary is in trouble?" Crystal asked.

"Let's not go back to arguing about Mary," Kenny said. He turned his eyes to the ceiling as his nostrils flared, and he took a deep breath in. "She knows how to take care of herself. She'd probably eat this thing for lunch."

"I'm going to signal for Dr. Firestine," Pat said. She tapped on her watch twice. The digital beep started strong and then slowly went out like a child's wind-up toy going dead.

"Has it ever sounded like that before?" Kenny asked.

"No," Pat said.

"Mine has. It was damaged during the last mission and stopped working," Crystal said.

Despair took over Pat's face. She dropped her arm like it was dead weight. "Great."

Crystal and Kenny brought up their wrists and tapped on their watches. The digital beeps were similar in sound, then both faded.

A solid knock came from the closed doorway, and everyone jumped two feet back. The electrical current used to close the doorway looked like it was being chipped away. Pieces of electricity popped off the doorway with each knock, and slowly drifted downward, then disappeared just before it touched the linoleum. It was like watching fireworks fall and fade away.

YOUR TURN:

1. What or who is knocking?

2. What is Mary doing on the other side now that she doesn't have her team?

3. Does Everett get up? If so, what does he do?

4. Define the word boondoggle. Does this word fit with the

story? Explain your answer.

5. Using your answers from above, finish the story.

CHAPTER 22
GLITTER CLUB
(Copacetic)

"Diana, why do you want to join Glitter Club?" Stephanie probed.

"Well, I love glitter for one," Diana said.

"How much do you love glitter?" Sierra asked, leaning into Diana's personal space.

The invasion of Diana's space allowed Sierra to take a closer look at her make-up. She'd been admiring it from afar, and this was her opportunity to get a better look. Glitter was clearly mixed in, which was a glittery gold star in Sierra's book.

"How long have you loved glitter?" Stephanie asked.

"My whole life," Diana said.

"Really? Interesting. I remember going to your 5th birthday

party, and I didn't see one spec of glitter. None," Stephanie said.

"My mother planned my 5th birthday party. I just got my tonsils out. I couldn't help with any planning. I was too sick," Diana explained.

"Fair enough," Sierra said.

"What types of glitter do you have at home?" Stephanie asked.

"I have 36 different types of single-color glitter. I have 13 pre-mixed glitters. I'm thinking of custom blending a fine pink glitter with a turquoise popsicle confetti," Diana said.

Oh, she's good, Stephanie thought. As Diana looked more and more relaxed with the interview questions, the whole atmosphere in the room became more fun and carefree, and Glitter Club added a new member.

Stephanie and Sierra exchanged smiles. "Welcome to glitter club!" they shouted in unison.

"O.M.G!" Diana yelled back.

The hugging frenzy lasted a few minutes. A new friendship with exciting possibilities sent jolts of energy into the room. If the energy were any higher, the glitter would start to levitate.

"Our glitter mix days are Wednesdays at my house," Stephanie said.

"I'll get your glitter smock ordered," Sierra said.

"Now we need to go through the glitter oath," Stephanie said.

"What's a glitter oath?" Diana asked.

"It's where we swear to keep all secrets, personal and glitter related. All custom glitter mixes belong to the club, and you can't duplicate it for your own purposes," Stephanie said.

"Oh," Diana said. Looking back and forth between Sierra and Stephanie, her smile turned down. "I thought we could just collaborate on mixing ideas and then use them as our own."

"What happens in Glitter Club, stays in Glitter Club," Stephanie said.

Contemplation and silence took over the room.

"You have to sign the oath also," Sierra said.

She put a piece of paper on the desk next to Diana. Glitter Club Oath was penned across the top in Sierra's best calligraphy.

"I have a lot of people willing to pay for custom glitter mixes; maybe we can start a business together and use Glitter Club for that," Diana suggested.

"That's not what this is," Stephanie said. "You can leave if you want, no hard feelings."

"No, I want to be in the club. No worries, I won't share with anyone," Diana said. Her voice a higher octave than normal.

Her eyes began to shift between the girls, and a small smile formed.

YOUR TURN:

1. Do you know anyone who loves glitter?

2. Does Diana end up signing the oath?

3. Will Diana use the club's glitter mixes for her own business?

4. Define the word copacetic. Does this word fit in the story? Explain your answer.

5. Using your answers from above, finish the story.

CHAPTER 23
HAPPY HUMAN
(Indignation)

If only life were simpler, I wouldn't be in this situation. The truth of the matter is, it is not simple, and I don't think it ever will be. Your life might be simple, and if it is, I'm happy for you.

That's a lie.

I'm not happy for you. I'm envious. And if I knew you, I'd probably be mean to you.

My happiness would be through the roof if my life were simple. I wouldn't be sitting in detention, rewriting my essay. I wasn't rewriting it because I'd lost it or because I didn't do it. It wasn't even because I didn't hand it in. I did.

This whole debacle was due to the universe clearly hating me. "You heard me, Universe. This is your fault, and I'm not taking that accusation back," I whispered through my teeth.

Mrs. Molly mole face gave her famous glare in my direction. "Do you need something, Heather?"

"Just a fair shake, but I'm guessing that's not within your abilities," I responded.

"Keep writing and no more talking," Mrs. Molly said.

I looked down at my paper without responding to her rudeness. This whole school was rude. I could not wait to get out of here. Since I started last year, I'd had nothing but problems with everyone.

The essay ordeal was just my latest. I honestly turned in my essay, which meant my teacher obviously lost it. There was no other explanation.

Sammy dropped his pencil, and it hit my foot. The lead made a slight scuff on my shoe. My. Brand. New. Shoes.

"Really? Do you not know how to hold a pencil?" I asked in a hushed voice.

"Sorry," Sammy said.

He held out his hand like he was expecting me to pick it up and give it to him. *What am I, his servant?* I kicked the pencil down the row of desks in front of us.

"Why would you do that?" Sammy asked.

"Why can't you hold a pencil?" I asked.

"You are a very rude person," Sammy said. "How would you feel if someone treated you the way you just treated me?"

"Mind your business," I said.

Sammy gave me a smirk and my nerves shattered with a blistering heat. How dare he smile at me after what I just said.

I watched him walk down the aisle and pick up his pencil. As he walked back to his seat, his eyes never left mine. Was he trying to break me? Please. My skin was way too thick.

"There has to be something inside of you that wants to be nice. A glimmer of good under all that anger," Sammy said.

"What is wrong with you?" I asked him. "I'm a nice person. I'm a good person, just not here."

"Really? I'd like to see that. Is there a specific geographical location that douses your horrible attitude and turns you into a happy people pleaser?" Sammy asked.

"You would never be invited to that geographical location," I retorted.

"I bet, by the end of the school year, I'm invited to your lair," Sammy said. "What's it like in there? Dark and creepy? Glitter and rainbows? A little of both?"

My brain waves swirled like clouds forming a tornado. This could not be happening.

"Stalking's never been cool," I said.

The bell rang, and I jumped out of my seat. Not bothering to put my stuff in my bag, I headed towards the door.

"See you tomorrow, happy human," Sammy said.

"Don't call me that!" I shouted without looking back.

YOUR TURN:

1. Describe how Heather acts at home.

2. Have you ever known someone like Heather, or have you acted like Heather?

3. Will Sammy try and talk to Heather the next day?

4. Define indignation. Does that word fit with the story? Explain your answer.

5. Using your answers from above, finish the story.

CHAPTER 24
DANNY'S RADIO
(Subterfuge)

"Hello! Can anyone hear me?" I yelled through my mic. "I'm stuck in… in… my room."

As I sat on the floor, my eyes wandered to each of the walls, inspecting every inch. Baseball cards were stacked neatly in their protective sleeves. Babe Ruth watched me as he stood motionless on the poster next to my bed. An unsigned bat was mounted above it. "One day, you'll sign that and give it to your son," my dad always said.

The mirror on my dresser reflected the baseball trophies opposite it. I won those a few years back when I was more interested in baseball. I used to throw the ball around every day.

It consumed all my time. It consumed my thoughts. It

consumed my entire life until the very second, my grandfather
gave me this radio and map.

Many people would be upset if they received a CB radio and
a map for their birthday, but not me. If my grandfather was
giving me these things, it was because they were very special.
They were two things he treasured, and when he handed them
down to me, he told me to never use them.

As odd as those instructions were, I never questioned them.
Afterall, it was Grandpa. He'd always been a little eccentric.

Instructions filled the back of the map. They weren't
normal instructions. They were all over the place. None of
them had numbers, no start, no finish. Some were written
upside down and some sideways.

The only thing my grandfather told me about the
instructions is that my destiny was not one path but all paths.
The path would be determined by which order I followed the
instructions. He also warned me that many of these paths
would lead to dangerous places.

"Why did you give this to me, Grandpa?" I whispered.

The mirror cracked, I shot up and twisted around before my
feet touched the ground. Facing the mirror, I took two steps
back, bumping into my meaningless trophies.

A swirling black dot, a half dollar in size, appeared. Black
tentacles thrashed out of the middle and started slapping the
mirror, pulling in all directions. The black vortex got bigger

and thinner.

I stretched my arm forward, compelled to touch it. *This could be my way out,* I thought. I took a quick breath and yanked my arm back. I was obviously delirious. *What if something is trying to come in?*

Shoving the radio and map into my backpack took about four seconds. I used the fifth second to grab my biggest, sturdiest trophy and got into position, ready to swing. My eyes were blurring as they strained to make out the first glimpse of whatever was coming through.

"Come on," I whispered. "Show yourself."

Nothing.

The tentacles calmed down when it reached the edges of the mirror. Black vapors moved like fog rolling down a hill out of the mirror. This was proof enough that it was a portal from somewhere to come into my bedroom.

My arms began to quiver a bit from holding the trophy for so long. I dropped my arms a bit and took a step to the side. I didn't want to be the bullseye directly in front of the mirror.

A muffled voice was talking in the distance. It was coming from everywhere, from outside my door, inside the mirror, from outside my window. I tried to open the door and the window, still no luck. The voice got louder and a bit clearer.

"Danny!" it yelled from inside the mirror.

A pounding noise startled me until I realized it was my own heart.

"Danny!" the voice yelled again.

My grandfather was yelling my name. The hairs on the back of my neck stood up.

Is that even possible?

I hadn't seen him in years.

YOUR TURN:

1. Have you ever loved a sport, activity, or club and then stopped participating or stopped liking it? Why?

2. Is the mirror a portal in, out, or both?

3. Describe how Danny used the radio and map to get into this predicament.

4. Define the word subterfuge. Does this word fit with the story? Explain your answer.

5. Using your answers from above, finish the story.

CHAPTER 25
NOT INVITED
(Snarky)

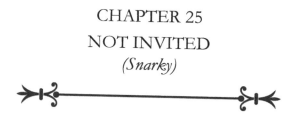

"Hey Chelsea," Amanda shouted as they passed in the hallway.

Chelsea nodded her head in acknowledgment. A small smile formed, and then she averted her eyes towards the floor. Tears welled up as she ducked into the bathroom.

She shut the stall door and grabbed a big wad of toilet paper. Her emotions came on like a buffalo stampede, and the tears cascaded in a freefall. She held the toilet paper in place so that her tears didn't mess up all of her make-up.

Stop crying. It doesn't matter. Chelsea tried to convince herself.

The bathroom door slowly creaked open, shoes squeaked across the floor, and ten steps later, a pair of red sneakers were directly in front of Chelsea's door.

"Chelsea?" Amanda asked.

Chelsea cleared her throat quick. "Yea?" she answered, trying to make her voice strong and nonchalant.

"Are you okay?" Amanda asked.

"Uh, yeah, I'm just going to the bathroom," Chelsea answered.

"Oh, okay. I'll wait for you then. We can walk to class together," Amanda said.

"No, that's okay," Chelsea said.

Blotting her face with wet toilet paper wasn't working well. She needed to pretend to finish her business anyway, so she grabbed more toilet paper and used it to wipe away the smeared mascara she imagined was there. She waited for Amanda to leave.

The red sneakers weren't directly in front of the door anymore. But Chelsea didn't hear them leave either or the sound of the door closing. So somewhere by the sinks, Amanda was waiting. *Why now?* Chelsea fretted.

Flushing the toilet gave her adequate noise and time to take three deep breaths without being overheard. Chelsea turned the silver lock on the stall door and walked out. She met Amanda's eyes for a few seconds, then pretended to be very interested in washing her hands.

She deliberately avoided looking in the mirror. If she didn't see what a mess she had become, neither could anyone else.

Amanda said nothing.

"So, what's up?" Chelsea said not able to stand the silence any longer.

"I know you're upset. It's pretty obvious, and I'm a good listener," Amanda said.

"Why are you so concerned?" Chelsea asked.

"Because I know how it feels to be left out. I know you weren't invited to Olive's party last night. I know that Olive doesn't treat you nicely, and you continue to hang out with her anyway," Amanda said.

Chelsea's eyes grew big as she brought them up to meet Amanda's. Her mouth parted slightly, and she froze for a brief moment. Anger rose to her cheeks, then flushed with embarrassment.

"Olive treated me the same way for many years. I don't know why I stayed friends with her for so long," Amanda continued. "I guess I was afraid that if I left Olive's group, I'd be alone. I don't like being alone."

"What made you stop being friends with her?" Chelsea asked.

"Willow came up to me one day, handed me a piece of chocolate, and offered me some sage advice. 'Food is an amazing thing to share with a friend. It gives us energy and life. Don't allow yourself to starve because you're waiting for a spot at someone else's table,'" Amanda said. "Willow and I are amazing friends now. We want to extend that friendship to you. You don't deserve to be treated the way Olive is treating you."

Chelsea nodded her head slowly as tears trickled down her cheeks.

Amanda grabbed Chelsea's hand and put a piece of chocolate in it. "Willow and I sit on the east side of the lunchroom. Come find us. I have more, much more where that came from," she said as she looked down at the sweet treat in Chelsea's hand.

Both girls gave a timid chuckle, and before Chelsea could move, Amanda gave her a quick hug and said, "See you in a few hours."

YOUR TURN:

1. Have you ever been in Chelsea's situation? If so, how did that feel?

2. Does Chelsea have lunch with Amanda and Willow?

3. How does Chelsea handle her relationship with Olive going forward?

4. Define the word snarky. Does this word fit with the story? Explain your answer.

5. Using your answers from above, finish the story.

CHAPTER 26
ALL WRONG
(Exasperated)

"You promised me that this would work," Ava said.

"Well, I totally thought it would," Emily replied.

"Give me the book. Let me look at the instructions," Ava ordered.

"Be careful. This is my great-grandmother's book. If it gets ruined, I'm dead," Emily pleaded.

"I seriously doubt you will be killed," Ava said.

"I was told that my life depends upon this book staying in one piece. If the pages rip or get torn out, I'm done for," Emily said.

"Parents say stuff like that all the time. They don't mean it literally," Ava said. "I promise I will be very careful."

Ava grabbed the book and flipped through the pages until she found their spell.

"It says that we should have stirred this potion clock-wise, not counter-clockwise," Ava said, holding the edge of the paper up and shaking it at Emily.

"Be careful," Emily said, grabbing the book.

Their eyes grew wide as they looked at each other's hands. Emily was holding the book, and Ava was holding the page.

"It came out so easily like it wasn't even attached," Ava said.

Emily grabbed the page and began to put it back into its place. "This page is so heavy," Emily said. "This book is getting so heavy."

"No!" Ava shouted. "It's you. You're disappearing."

Tears began to pour from Emily's eyes as she reached for Ava, but before they locked hands, she was gone. The book fell with a thud, and Ava jumped at the dust rising from the cover.

This wasn't a normal waft of dust. Particles were swirling together in unison like a marching band walking to a beat. They rose and stretched out until the bottom of the dust tornado was touching the book on the floor and the ceiling.

Ava took a couple stumbling steps back and quickly shut her mouth when she could taste old book pages on her tongue. She grabbed a cloth and placed it around her mouth and nose to keep whatever it was away from her insides.

"Help me, Ava," a small voice whispered.

"Emily!" Ava shouted. "How?"

"Find my grandma, Harriet. Give her the book." Emily's voice was fading. "Hurry!"

The dust disappeared in an instant, leaving no trace.

"Ok, so, this is bad. Real bad," Ava said, staring at the book for a moment before giving herself a pep talk. "Dang, it. I can do this. I can totally do this."

Nudging the book with her foot, she got no reaction. Feeling it was safe, or safe enough, she picked up the book gingerly and slowly placed it in her backpack, making sure it was nice and tight. In no way could she let that thing flop around and get damaged anymore.

Thankfully, she didn't have to ride her bike too far. She pedaled with everything she had to the church. Emily's grandmother was always there on Wednesdays. She'd know what to do.

Without bothering to come to a complete stop, she jumped off of her bike and let it fall where it wanted. The crash made the churchgoers turn and look her way, for just a brief moment, anyway.

People were everywhere, crowding the paths and making it difficult to walk through the front doors of John the Baptist

Church. Ava didn't stop to look around or give the greeters the attention they wanted. She had more important things to do.

Her stride was steady with each pew she passed. Her heart was very aware of the story she was about to tell Grandma Harriet. The backdoor was in front of her before she knew it. She stumbled down the steps and straight into the church graveyard.

Only a handful of people were walking around and paying their respects.

"Not too many witnesses," Ava whispered. "I can tell my story to Grandma Harriet quietly, and hopefully, she won't be mad enough to cause a scene."

YOUR TURN:

1. Where exactly is Grandma Harriet at, in the graveyard?

2. Describe the relationship between Grandma Harriet and Emily.

3. Write the dialogue between Ava and Grandma Harriet, where Ava is explaining what happened.

4. Define the word exasperated. Will exasperated be an appropriate description of what Grandma Harriet will

feel when she finds out what happened? Explain your answer.

5. Using your answers above, finish the story.

CHAPTER 27
CLICK CLICK
(Agog)

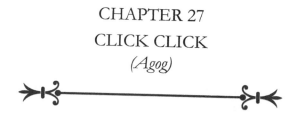

"The last number is 18," Tom said.

"Okay," Ben replied, steadying his hand before he moved the dial.

The last two clicks on the combination lock created more anxiety than even Ben's little brother could instill, after shouting he was car sick while Ben was trapped in the backseat with him.

A gentle tug on the safe's handle revealed a mistake had been made. Ben tugged a bit harder, and the door still refused to open. Pushing on the safe door in frustration didn't make it budge either. It stood its ground like it was designed to do.

Cobwebs clung to the corners of the black safe and made a blanket of silk that connected to the bookshelves nestled all around it. The safe had been hidden for centuries behind a tidy stack of books.

Those same books now lay in a crumbled mess on the floor, having been pushed aside, no longer able to hide their owner's secret. A treasure lay inside this safe that the owner hadn't take with him. A treasure that must now be taken.

"What went wrong?" Tom asked.

"I don't know," Ben said.

"Let me try," Tom offered.

"Go for it," Ben said and moved out of the way. "If we don't get this, we have no way to free Isabelle."

"I'm aware of that. We were given the same information after they paired us up. I know the importance," Tom said.

"I know you know. I was just stressing it out of frustration, I suppose," Ben said. "Sorry."

The dial whirled in circles like a Ferris wheel on turbo juice. Sweaty fingers grabbed the knob on the dial. "First number?" Tom asked.

"24," Ben said.

Tom could hear the clicking, which seemed to be the signal for his hands to begin to shake. Taking a deep calming breath, he steadied himself.

"Okay," Tom said. "Next."

"13"

What seemed like endless clicking came to an abrupt stop at thirteen.

"Last number?" Tom asked.

"18," Ben said. He let out a sigh as a burp jumped out of his mouth like a toad's tongue leaping for a fly.

"Dude, disgusting," Tom grimaced. "That stinks."

"You didn't have to drink the concoction to get this combination. I did. It wasn't a tasty little treat made of sugar and spice," Ben hissed.

"Sorry," Tom said. "What was the last number again?"

"18," Ben said.

The clicking was slow and deliberate. Each resounding click caused a pause in their breathing. The anticipation was palpible.

Pulling at the door handle, a loud clang rung in their ears. The handle jerked towards the floor as the last clang rung. Their lungs forced them to breathe even though their hearts froze.

Tom pulled the door towards him. They winced at the creak of the hinges, but their eyes were glued to the contents in the safe. Red velvet lined the shelves. Once so plush and vivid, now it lay dull, matted, and frail.

YOUR TURN:

1. Is the situation they're in real or part of a game?

2. What's in the safe?

3. How and why did Tom and Ben get paired up?

4. Define the word agog. Does this word describe what Tom and Ben are feeling during the story? Explain your answer.

5. Using your answers above, finish the story.

CHAPTER 28
CREAKY STAIRS
(Imprudent)

Jill slammed the door behind them. They were now trapped, three stories up, on the stoop of a rickety old house with an even more rickety staircase in front of them.

"Well, this is horrible," Chuck said, panting from all the running they just did.

"It will be okay," Jill said.

"Really? Are you kidding me?" Chuck asked.

"I'm sure we will be okay." Jill hesitated. "Well, pretty sure."

Quick nods up and down were all she could do at this point. She was keeping an eye on the ground, that was far enough to cause alarm, trying to figure out the best way out of their predicament. That, and trying not to let the rising panic overcome her.

"What are we supposed to do now? Chuck said. He began to wipe his sweaty palms on his pants and planted his back firmly against the siding.

"We can't go back in, that's for sure," Jill said. "We have to go down."

"You think we should go down those stairs? There's no way we are going to make it," Chuck said.

"It's our only choice. You can stay up here. I'm going," Jill said.

As her right foot touched the first stair, a groan that only an evil spirit could make burst from under the door. Black mist began to cozy up to Chuck's feet, and he took the lead going down the stairs.

"The faster we go, the better," he said.

"I don't know about that," Jill replied.

Chuck was now five steps ahead of Jill and was on the first landing. He only had to go one more flight of stairs before he was safely on the ground.

The moaning became a wicked laugh. Wood creaked underneath Chuck, and his eyes were the first to show alarm. A trap door at landing two opened up and swallowed Chuck whole.

Jill froze. Her breathing stopped until Chuck's screams

could no longer be heard. The abrupt silence jolted her back to the present.

Jill used the railing to catapult herself over the first landing and onto the steps below. She was now between landing one and the ground. Close enough, it would be plenty safe to jump off the stairs and not get hurt. Maybe a little hurt, but she wouldn't die.

The stairs began to shake, and Jill could see hinges appearing to make the stairs open. It was now or never. With a tight grip on the railing, Jill thrust herself up and over.

She landed hard then rolled. The pain in her ankle was not greater than the panic in her chest. She kept moving towards the front gates.

Spotlights burst on like firecrackers on the fourth of July. Jill's eyes struggled to open; her hand shielded the direct light, trying to assassinate her vision.

"You made it out of the house. That's notable but not a great feat by any means," a man's voice said from behind the lights.

Panting and trying to stand, she replied, "Who are you? I need help getting my friend!"

"He's fine. My team is already getting him out of the house," the man said. "You show promise, my dear."

"What?" Jill asked.

"We'll talk more later. You can count on that," he said.

YOUR TURN:

1. Why are Chuck and Jill in the house?

2. Create the scene where Chuck and Jill enter the house.

3. Who is the mysterious man at the end of the story, and what does he want?

4. Define the word imprudent. Does this word fit any of the characters in the story? Explain your answer.

5. Using your answers above, finish the story.

CHAPTER 29
GUM WRAPPER
(Fortitude)

"I think this is significant," Clyde said.

"A gum wrapper?" George looked at him like he was crazy. "How?"

"I don't know yet," Clyde said.

A crinkled up waxy pink square lay on the ground. It lay ten feet from the swing set and only inches away from the bike path.

"Fine, I'll put it with the other pieces," George said.

George's sticky fingers rolled the wrapper into a small ball, then slam-dunked it into a red and white backpack. His victory dance needed work, but his enthusiasm was NFL playoff material.

"Do you think we are going to find more?" George asked.

"Maybe," Clyde said.

"We will, I know it," George said. His hand slapped the back of Clyde's blue jacket.

"Ouch, and thanks," Clyde said. "Let's follow the path."

"Okay, my friend," George said. "We are going to win this."

The energy George had was not only for the pink wrapper but for the journey. He was one of those friends that could never be dampened with the anxieties of life. A true 'go with the flow' kind of guy.

Not only did the bike path have major amounts of trash, but it was also overrun with dog poop. The stink took little jabs at their noses, and they were forced to cover their nose and mouth with their sleeves. Once they reached the crossroads in the path, a whirlwind breeze accosted their noses regardless of how thick their shirts were.

"This is it. This is the spot," Clyde said.

"This is going to be a challenge," George said. "I'm game if you are. Are you really up for this?"

"Yes. I said I would be part of this, and I'm always true to my word," Clyde said.

"Okay, let's make the calls," George said.

Thirty minutes went by before footsteps and chatter could

be heard.

"No one touches anything until it's been filmed!" George yelled. "Who's got the camera? We need a before and after."

"I've got it!" A lady in all black yelled. "Everyone, move to the other side. Stay behind the camera." A slow turn with a couple close up's, a lengthy aerial view, and she had captured the area and all its filth.

"Attention! Attention!" A man in all black yelled through a megaphone. "When you hear the gunshot, you have 72 hours to get this area cleaned up and looking amazing. There are three groups fighting for first place. The winner will be the group whose site looks the best. The reward is $100,000. This will go into a scholarship fund for all of you to share equally."

Bang!

Everyone scattered at the sound. The trash takers whipped out their pokers and stabbed away. Poop patrol was gloved and masked up. Landscaping ladies began pulling weeds, and the engineer eagle scouts began planning for benches in the center of what would be a spectacular round-a-bout.

YOUR TURN:

1. Describe all the rules in this game.

2. Describe where the other two groups chose to clean up

or change.

3. Describe a scene where Clyde is working with one of the groups?

4. Define the word fortitude. Does Clyde have fortitude? Explain your answer.

5. Using your answers above, finish the story.

CHAPTER 30
RAINDROP
(Intrigue)

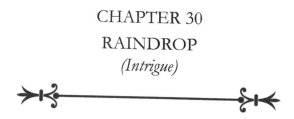

Eight dusty bottles lined up perfectly on top of a rickety wooden shelf. The shelves below were littered with papers, that at one time, were in the leather journal that was lying on the ground. Long ago, it was probably bound very nicely with elegant gold trim on the edges and a lovely engraving on the back.

From what I could see, the papers that were in disarray had coffee stains, oil spots, and smudge marks everywhere. Then there were the mystery marks. My mom wouldn't go into detail on the mystery marks, only that it wasn't a subject she was willing to discuss at this time.

Normally, I would have put some gloves on and gotten to work deciphering what this was. My curiosity wasn't for the faint of heart. Apparently, my father agreed because he put a metal mesh barricade up, blocking me from touching all those mysterious items.

Using my flashlight, notepad, and pen I found in Great Aunt Melva's junk drawer, I began documenting what I could see.

"Bottle number one," I said out loud. "Tall, greenish bottle. Looks like one I've seen olive oil in at the store."

Moving onto the next bottle, my mind began to wander to Aunt Melva. It was so sad what had happened to her. I felt bad, and yet I never even knew her. She never once came to visit.

My parents didn't talk about her much. To be honest, I don't think they really talked about her at all. A comment here and there, but that was it. I remember Mom coming into my bedroom a few nights back to tell me about the accident. I wasn't sure how to feel because I had no idea who she was.

Being here, though, I felt a connection to her. Maybe it was because I was surrounded by her things. The dirty clothes I was standing on had been lining the floor since who knows when. As gross as this basement was, I didn't feel like I was intruding. I felt like I belonged.

"Rae?" My mom yelled from the top of the stairs.

"Yea?" I yelled back.

"If you're going to be down there, you need to clean it. We only have a few more days to get everything out of this house and ready to sell," Mom yelled.

"Okay. I can take care of these shelves too, if Dad can move this metal barricade," I shouted back.

"Good try! Dad will handle the shelf; you work on the junk. Throw away everything that has mold on it," Mom yelled.

"Okay," I said.

"Apparently, I'll be throwing everything away," I said to myself. "But first, I must catalog."

Back to bottle number two. Black. But it looked like it was painted black. The topper was a round ball of sorts.

The memory of the mystery movie I watched last week kicked in, and I began making verbal notes to my partner.

"Bottle number three," I said loudly. "Yes, this is so curious. Curious indeed. Bottle number three is a triangle. Even the lid is pointy. Hmmm… it looks cool, but does it serve a purpose?"

"Yes," Dad said from behind me.

I swung around, heart pounding. "I didn't hear you come down the stairs," I said.

"I can tell," he said.

"Okay, why's that bottle a triangle?" I asked.

"Back in the day, bottles that had poisonous things in them

had to be pointy or have rough or ribbed edges so that even in the dark, you wouldn't mistake them for a regular medicine bottle," Dad said.

My eyes went back around to look at the bottle. "That has poison in it?" I asked. "What kind?"

"I don't know what's in it," Dad said. "We need to figure that out, so we know how to get rid of them safely," Dad said.

With our noses about a foot from the barricade, we watched the bottles as if they might start talking to us. My brain made a discovery, and I blinked several times before I could even interpret what I was seeing.

A light green bottle sat at the end of the shelf. It looked like it had been wiped off and was now shiny and new. The sticker was old but legible. *Raindrops from the window seal of Rae Aerrasmith.*

"Dad?" I said, pointing to the bottle.

"I saw that earlier. It's why I put the barricade up. I don't know why it's there or what's really in it," he said. "Aunt Melva's sister, Milly, is coming over tonight to figure all this out."

"I have a Great Aunt Milly?" I asked. "Why don't I know any of this?"

"That's why," he said, pointing at my bottle.

YOUR TURN:

1. Write a brief bio on who Great Aunt Melva is.

2. Why does she have a bottle of raindrops from Rae' Aerrasmith's window seal?

3. Finish the inventory list that Rae was creating. Describe each bottle and what's inside.

4. Define the word intrigue. Does this fit Rae? Explain your answer.

5. Using your answers above, finish the story.

CHAPTER 31
LUNCH LADY LUNACY
(Scheme)

"These cookies are amazing," Amity said.

"Right! I'm getting another one," Tamera said. She jumped out of her chair and skipped to the lunch counter with the bounce of a baby goat.

"She's hyper," Ralph said. His thumb pointing in Tamera's direction.

"It's these cookies, I think. They just make me so happy. You should try one," Amity said.

She shoved one in Ralph's face, and he backed away like she had the plague.

"What's wrong with you?" Amity asked. "You're afraid of my cookie? I didn't lick it. I swear."

"It's not that. I'm allergic to dairy. I can't even touch it," Ralph explained.

"Yeah, Ralph will blow up like a balloon if he eats dairy, not to mention the crazy rash he'll get if he even touches it," Tamera said from behind them.

"That sucks! I'm sorry," Amity said.

"It's okay. I'm used to dealing with it," Ralph said.

Brown curly hair that looked like it was battling itself lay on top of Ralph's head. When he was contemplating something, he ran his fingers through it. It was like the battle got retold, and another section of his hair got to win with each thought. This battle seemed to get worse as he sat there.

"What are you thinking about?" Tamera asked with a mouth full of cookie.

"Look around," Ralph said. "Everyone is eating these cookies."

"They're good," Amity said.

"Yes, yes they are," Tamera agreed.

"It's odd. Every single person is eating them. No one's even eating their lunches. It's just these cookies," Ralph said.

"I think they're great," Amity said, licking the chocolate from her finger.

"Yes, yes they are," Tamera agreed, again.

Ralph's eyes were glued to the girls, and the girl's eyes were glued to their cookies. Standing up to get a better look at the lunchroom, he noticed that it was a feeding frenzy. Some kids had ten cookies in front of them. Some were sucking the chocolate off their fingers, and some were trying to bribe their friends for cookies or money to buy more cookies.

BZZZZZZ!

The lunch bell went off and startled everyone from their feast. Groans could be heard, and backpacks were filled with uneaten cookies. Lunches were thrown in the trash as everyone filed out of the lunchroom.

The only legs that were left belonged to Ralph, and they slowly turned towards the cookie stand sitting by the register. His curiosity couldn't be squelched, and he found himself face to face with Mrs. Laney.

"Can I help you?" She asked. "I have a cookie if you want. Two dollars."

"No, thanks," Ralph said. "Weren't they only a dollar last month?"

"Things change. Here, just try one," Mrs. Laney said.

"No," Ralph said. He looked up and noticed a handmade poster on the wall noting the number of cookies sold, the amount of money saved, and a big cruise ship.

"You've got some wandering eyes, Ralph. If you don't want to buy anything, you'll need to leave," Mrs. Laney said.

"What are you putting in those cookies?" Ralph asked.

"You're being silly!" Mrs. Laney laughed so hard, the quarter-sized mole on her neck seemed to change shape as the jowls of her throat jostled with each bellow.

In an instant, her laugh stopped, the mole froze, and she yelled. "Get out of my lunchroom!"

YOUR TURN:

1. Are these cookies so good that the kids want more, or is there something in the cookies to create an addiction to them?

2. What will Ralph do next?

3. Does the lunch lady reach her goal and get to go on the cruise?

4. Define the word scheme. Does this fit with what the lunch lady is doing? Explain your answer.

5. Using your answers above, finish the story.

CHAPTER 32
CLIMBING ROPE
(Spiteful)

"My hands are so sweaty right now. I just don't think I can do this. I mean, I totally would, but the sweat is just out of control," Donny said.

"There's like twenty people ahead of us. Just rub them on your shorts. You'll be fine," Jeff said.

"Fine? Can you see this?" Donny asked.

Donny raised his sweaty hands to Jeff's eye level. A slight shake could be detected, and Jeff sighed. "You don't have to be afraid. If you can't climb the rope, you can't climb it," Jeff said.

"I'm not afraid," Donny said, rubbing his hands on his shorts. "How absurd is this, though. Why do we have to show our teacher that we can climb a rope? It's degrading to every student. Every single one. We shouldn't have to prove these types of things."

Whoosh!

A ball zipped past Donny's head, slightly brushing his already rosy cheeks. He jumped away from the danger, and his chest heaved for air.

"Gannon Fick!" Mr. White shouted.

All eyes bounced back and forth between Gannon and Mr. White.

"Keep the balls on that side," Mr. White said. The stare between them lasted longer than it should have, and it wasn't Mr. White that broke the gaze.

"Yes, sir," Gannon said as he turned to look at Donny.

The corners of Gannon's mouth rose slightly, and he nodded his head a bit towards Donny. After a few seconds, Gannon turned and started shooting hoops again.

"Don't let him intimidate you," Jeff said.

"Easy for you to say. Gannon Fick is a monster, and he's been after me since kindergarten," Donny said. "Okay, so, there are ten people in front of us now, and we only have 15 mins left. I'm going out on a limb and saying, we won't be doing this today."

"I really wanted to get this done and over with," Jeff said.

"I'm surprised she can climb the rope," Donny said, watching one of their classmates climb the rope with ease. "Her arms are so scrawny."

Donny and Jeff watched as Lolli climbed and climbed and climbed.

"Wow," Jeff said.

"Wow is right," Donny replied.

A slap on the shoulder and Donny jolted out of his thoughts.

"She's got bigger muscles than you," Gannon said while holding onto the back of Donny's neck.

Jeff whacked Gannon's arm, and it went flying back.

Gannon's eyes grew wide in surprise, as did Jeff and Donny's. Jeff was shaking, but his voice was strong and steady. "Back off."

"How much did you pay for your bodyguard?" Gannon shouted and began to laugh, almost convincingly.

"Mr. Fick!" shouted Mr. White. "Locker room and detention."

The fake laugh trailed off as Gannon walked towards the locker room. He shouted, "Worth it!" without looking back.

All attention went back onto the rope.

"Five people and only four minutes left. Not today, I say, not today," Donny said. His sweaty palms began to dry, and a smile appeared as he grabbed Jeff's arm and shook it.

YOUR TURN:

1. Does Jeff get out of climbing the rope today?

2. Write the scene where Donny is climbing the rope.

3. Explain why Donny and Gannon don't get along.

4. Define the word spiteful. Does that word fit Gannon? Explain your answer.

5. Using your answers above, finish the story.

CHAPTER 33
ARMCHAIR
(Despondent)

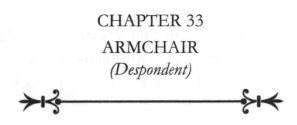

A faded brown leather armchair sat all alone amongst the new furniture. The common area was a place for friends to gather during breaks and study. People sat on, laid on, jumped on, and slid off of the new furniture day in and day out.

The armchair was ignored like the plague, and it all started two years ago today when Jennifer plopped down on it and was surprised with the biggest Whoopee cushion of her life. The fart noise was so loud, people swear they could smell something disturbing, but it was all a gag. That fart noise ruined Jennifer's social life, as well as a perfectly good armchair. No one wants to sit in a fart chair.

Jennifer had her friends start a petition to get the chair removed from the school. It had 247 votes as of today. The principal informed Jennifer's friends that they needed 300 total before he would honor their request.

"Why are you so obsessed with saving this chair?" May asked.

"I think it's a great chair. It's been here forever, and I think it needs to stay," Hattie said.

"So, your feeling nostalgic?" May asked.

"Sort of, I suppose," Hattie said.

"Tell me the real reason," May said.

"Well, you know how my parents are getting a divorce?" Hattie asked.

"Yes," May said.

"This chair is where they met, like twenty years ago. My mom was sitting in the chair, and my dad sat on the arm so they could get a picture together for the yearbook. They didn't even know each other, but that picture and this chair gave them something to talk about. Sparks flew, and here I am," Hattie said.

"Oh. I get it now. Makes sense," May said.

Tears were threatening to spill from Hattie's eyes, but she fought them back by looking up and waiting for the tears to back off.

May rested her head on Hattie's shoulder, then sprung back up. "Let's save this chair!" May shouted, startling those around them, including Hattie.

A single tear escaped but was quickly wiped away. "How are we going to do that?" Hattie asked.

"Rumors. It's what I'm good at," May said.

"Really?" Hattie said. "We are like best friends, and I didn't know this."

"Well, that's what makes me so good. I'm here for you," May said.

"Hey," May shouted at Jed, who was trying to squeeze by us.

"What?" He asked.

"Did you know that this chair is how our football team won all those games back in the '90s?" Hattie asked.

"What are you talking about?" Jed asked.

"Well, you guys haven't won much, and in the '90s, there was a ginormous winning streak because each player sat in the chair and visualized the win. It's a superstitious football ritual," May said.

Jed's face crinkled a little bit as his eyes studied the chair.

"You're the captain of the football team, and you've never heard of this? That's weird," May said. "You guys need all the help you can get. Maybe you need to reenact the tradition so we can start winning," May said.

Jed nodded slowly as contemplation began to turn the wheels inside his football dreams.

"Have a great day," May said as she pulled Hattie down that hallway.

"Wow, that was great. I mean, I had no idea about that tradition," Hattie said. "It really worked?"

May stopped tugging at Hattie and looked into her eyes. "Are you messing with me?" May asked.

"Um," Hattie responded.

"Okay, you're not. That was the rumor, Hattie. If the football team uses the chair and needs it, the chair won't go anywhere," May explained.

"You're a genius!" Hattie shouted.

YOUR TURN:

1. Have you ever started a rumor?

2. Do you think May's rumor will work to save the chair?

3. How do you think Jennifer will feel if May's rumor works?

4. Define the word despondent. Does this fit Hattie when she thinks about her parents? Explain your answer.

5. Using your answers above, finish the story.

CHAPTER 34
I DON'T KNOW
(Veracity)

"Leon, what are you doing?" Alfred asked.

"I don't know, zoning out, I suppose," Leon said.

"Aren't you supposed to be at baseball practice?" Alfred asked.

"Yep, I'll talk to you later. Gotta go," Leon said and quickly dashed off.

As Leon's stocky body passed by each locker, it was as if his legs were getting heavier with each step. His right shoulder slid along the wall like it was a magnet, not able to break free. Bumping into the drinking fountain rattled his thoughts, and he was not sure where he was.

"Leon?" Megan asked from behind.

A swift turn and he almost fell. He caught himself on the fountain and then leaned against the wall to keep his balance.

"What's wrong?" Megan asked.

"I don't know, I'm just trying to get to baseball practice," Leon said. "What's wrong with you?"

"Nothing's wrong with me," Megan said.

"Okay then, I need to get to practice," Leon said.

Leon patted the wall when he made it past the drinking fountain. One hand always on the wall. It was as if he needed it in order to stay upright.

"Leon! Baseball practice is that way," Megan said, pointing to the hallway on his left.

A slight wave of thanks was all that was returned to Megan.

Alfred caught up to Megan and their eyes locked. When they looked back down the hall, they not only searched first for words but also the strength to do what they knew had to be done.

"What's going on with him?" Megan asked.

"I don't know, but I've seen him like this a few times since his dad left," Alfred said. "Should we say something?"

"I don't know. I think we should, but I don't want him to get in trouble," Megan said.

"Me either, but what if he's acting like this because of some chemical imbalance or something? That's serious, and we need to help him," Alfred said.

"I don't know. If he's on his way to practice, won't the coach notice and do something?" Megan asked.

"Maybe, but who knows. Maybe not," Alfred said.

"Haven't other people noticed? Don't you think someone else has already said something?" Megan asked.

"You're probably right. We can't be the only ones to have seen something," Alfred said.

Silence crept in between them. The halls had never been so lonely.

Megan cleared her throat. "Although my mom always says better safe than sorry. If something bad happens to him that we could have stopped…I don't know if I would be able to live with myself."

"True. He's supposed to be my friend, and I need to do whatever it takes to help him," Alfred said.

The sound of paper shuffling came from inside Mrs. Maple's classroom. Megan and Alfred looked at each other and then at the door. Deep breaths seemed to clutter the hallway with noise, and they walked through the door.

YOUR TURN:

1. Create a dialogue between Alfred, Megan, and Mrs. Maples.

2. How will Alfred, Megan, and Leon's relationship change, if at all?

3. What would you have done?

4. Define the word veracity. Does this word fit Megan and Alfred? Explain your answer.

5. Using your answers above, finish the story.

CHAPTER 35
RAT-A-ROO
(Newfangled)

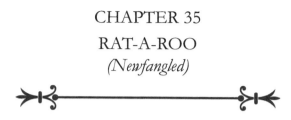

I'm going on the record here and letting you know that I did not create this animal. I did not wish this animal into existence. I didn't steal it from a science lab. It came to me. I want to make that very clear. Maybe it had a sixth sense and knew I would protect it or something. It chose me, and it's mine, and I'm not giving it back.

What are the odds that it would just find me of all people to be friends with? The park was loaded with kids, and parents, and huggy, kissy families. Animals liked that stuff, but this little guy passed them all by and came straight for me.

That's basically how it all happened. Me sitting under a tree on my backpack, watching others have fun. I was waiting for my friend to show up but having major doubts that he would since his mom found out he got an F in math. I was holding out, though, and wanted to wait a little while longer just in case.

My eyes were roaming all over the place, looking for any sign of Gilly. He was pretty sneaky, so I could totally see him conning his mom into letting him come and then sneaking up on me like a lion sneaking up on its prey. He was a trickster, and anytime I got the better of him, I bragged way longer than I should because it just didn't happen very often. None the less, we were great friends.

As my eyes investigated the tree line on the other side of the play equipment, I noticed something moving ever so slightly. It was small, like a plump squirrel but without the tail. The squirrels in my neighborhood loved to jump in front of moving vehicles, so my brain wasn't telling me it was weird or anything like that. It was just missing a tail from an unfortunate incident.

The little thing was bouncing back and forth between two trees, staying low. But for some odd reason, I felt like it was trying to get my attention. When I looked away, it would jump around, and when I would stare at it, it would be still. And as far as I could tell, it was staring back at me.

I began to debate on whether or not to go over there and check it out. It was strange enough that I couldn't not check it out. It was also strange enough, I thought I just better take a stick or something, if you know what I mean.

Walking around the tree, I found plenty of sticks that would be great for toy soldier forts, but nothing I would consider big enough to protect me. My next plan was a book.

Not really ideal, because I could hear my mom saying, 'Oliver, if I have to pay for one more damaged schoolbook… you're grounded for life.' But my next thought was, if I had to ruin the book to save my own life from a rabid, tailless squirrel, she should understand.

I knelt down next to my bag and pulled out my history book. This book was about the Civil War, and I was getting ready to possibly go to war with a weird squirrel, so I thought it was fitting. It was also the thickest and heaviest book in my arsenal. I slung my backpack over my shoulder and stood, book in hand.

Scoping out the tree line, the little animal was gone. *Oh, that figures.* I was still shaking a bit from being nervous, but after I went to all this trouble making a plan, I was a bit disappointed that the crazy little thing was gone.

I lowered my shoulder, and my bag plopped down onto the ground with a thud. It also made a little squeak. Which was weird because I didn't have anything that would have squeaked. Like, nothing.

The hairs on the back of my neck stood up. My grip tightened on my book. My eyes bugged out, and my body tensed. My heart was jumping around like it was in a pinball machine, and the player was on a roll. I held my book out in front of me like a shield.

My mistake was when I took a step back and tripped over my backpack. As I was going down, I could see this little thing coming at me, but it wasn't a squirrel. My brain couldn't process what it was. I saw brown beaver fur with kangaroo legs and a face and body like a rat. My brain switched from figuring out this puzzle to, I'm going to die.

Clearly, I didn't die.

When I sat up, it was next to my leg, and for whatever reason, it seemed to be smiling at me. It was kind of cute even with the rat-like teeth. It hopped on my leg like a tiny little kangaroo then made a squeaky noise.

I was sweating uncontrollably. It was only like 50 degrees outside, so I couldn't blame it on that. My heart was refusing to slow down, but somehow, I knew this little thing was friendly.

I let it smell my hand, and then he began to rub his head on my fingers. He was begging me to pet him. I couldn't refuse. We began our friendship, that very moment.

YOUR TURN:

1. If you found a new species of animal, what would it look and act like?

2. Does Oliver tell his family about Rat-A-Roo, or does he keep it a secret?

3. What obstacles would Oliver face with having a new species of animal to care for?

4. Define the word newfangled. Does that word fit in this story? Explain your answer.

5. Using your answers above, finish the story.

CHAPTER 36
PAPAYA PIZZA
(Timid)

"I am now a master pizza maker!" Jake boasted from the kitchen.

"I've been waiting forever," Elayna said. "I want to be the first to try it."

"Okay, okay, my crazy followers," Jake said. He held up the small pizza, pretending that a crowd of crazed pizza lovers was trying to get at him. "Everyone will get a slice in time. Please, no need to rush me."

"Woo!" Elayna shouted. "I don't know if I can handle this crowd you've attracted."

Both of them laughed as Jake set his pizza on the kitchen table and began to cut slices.

"This looks really cool," Elayna said. "What is that?"

"It's papaya," Jake said. "I think you'll like it."

"I do like pineapple on my pizza, so why not papaya?" Elayna supposed.

"After we watched Chef and the Mess last weekend, I was inspired to make something fun like this," Jake said. "Eat up."

The pizza looked hot and steamy with paper-thin slices of papaya and pepper jack cheese. It was thin crust and baked perfectly, so it was crunchy and nowhere close to burnt.

Elayna pulled one of the slices away from its group, and the cheese was refusing to part with the others. She had to use her fingers to break the connection. Just the way she liked her pizza.

Jake watched as she blew on her slice and then took a bite. Her head shook from side to side as she had to break the gooey cheese apart. Then something weird happened. He noticed a quizzical look move onto her face.

"What's going on?" Jake asked. "Tell me. You hate it? What?"

Grabbing for a napkin with one hand, she held a finger up from her other hand. She shook her head, then covered her mouth with the napkin.

"Oh no, this can't be happening. Are you spitting it out? This is horrible. I'm ruined," Jake said. He started to pace. "I knew I would never make it as a master chef. It's just not in the cards."

With a big gulp, the bite of papaya pizza was down. Jake studied her face and then asked, "Well?"

"It's not that it's…bad," Elayna said.

"Really? You're going to start with that? That is a dead give-a-way that it's horrible," Jake wailed.

"It's not! It's not bad! I swear. I just think it's not for me," Elayna said. "Let's have some other people taste it. I bet you there are a lot of people that will love it."

"No way am I doing that. You not liking it is hard enough. I can't take that risk of someone else not liking it. I can't do that. You know I'm not brave like that. I'd literally die if other people found out," Jake said.

"Found out what? That you have a wide range of tastes and likes? That you like to experiment and be adventurous with your food? That you're not boring?" Elayna asked. "Jake, you are a chef. Being a chef means not everyone will love your food. Just because my taste buds are not as open as yours doesn't mean it's bad."

"Hey guys, what are you doing?" Jake's dad asked.

"Try Jake's pizza," Elayna said.

"No," Jake said, reaching for the plate it was on.

"Sweet," Jake's dad said. He grabbed a slice before Jake

could stop him. "Oh man, this is great!"

Jake looked towards the floor. "You are obligated to say that since you're my dad."

Elayna grabbed the plate and took off running like a rabbit being chased by a coyote. Out the front door and down the street she went. Jake was so startled by what she was doing, it took him several seconds to get his feet moving, but he was slowly catching up.

Oh, no. Don't do this. Please don't go there. Yep, she's going there, Jake's inner voice panted. "NO!" Jake shouted. It was too late.

The doorbell to Mr. Mead's house was ringing. The local food critique was opening the door as Jake stumbled up the stairs.

"Yes?" Mr. Mead asked.

"My friend Jake just made an amazing pizza, and we would be honored to get your opinion on it," Elayna blurted out.

Jake had to sit back and just suck it up because he would, under no circumstances, cause a scene in front of Mr. Mead. He was legendary in the community.

Mr. Mead looked at them both, then took the plate. He raised the plate to eye level and inspected the crust. He tugged on the cheese. A corner of the papaya was lifted and then placed back down. His nose leaned in and inhaled the aroma.

"Interesting," Mr. Mead said.

Jake's eyes grew to softballs as Mr. Mead picked up a slice of papaya pizza and took a bite.

"Mmmm, very interesting," Mr. Mead said. "I can taste so many flavors. Yes, you are a chef in the making. I can taste the potential. Come in, both of you. Let's talk."

YOUR TURN:

1. If Mr. Mead were to write a review, what would it say?

2. Do you think Jake is mad at Elayna for taking the pizza to Mr. Mead?

3. How would you tell a friend that you didn't like something they made?

4. Define the word timid. Does this word fit Jake? Explain your answer.

5. Using your answers above, finish the story.

CHAPTER 37
TRUE FRIENDS
(Steadfast)

"Why are you friends with her?" Liz asked.

"We've always been friends," Carol said.

"But look at her," Liz said.

Liz pointed at a pair of oversized glasses, masking the face of a mousy brown-haired girl. A book covered the rest of her face as she sat in the corner of the library, completely engrossed in her book.

"Debby is a total nerd. A loser," Liz said.

"No, actually she's not. She's been there for me since we were in kindergarten," Carol said. "She may not fit in with the popular group, but it doesn't make her a loser."

"You, being friends with her, makes you not fit into the

popular group either. You want to be part of our group, you've got to kick Debby the dork to the curb," Liz said.

Carol looked at Debby, laughing at whatever science fiction book she was reading. Her lips moved whenever she read.

She ate peanut butter and banana sandwiches not because she liked them, but because Elvis, the King of Rock and Roll, liked them. Her clothes rarely matched or fit right, and some days, she'd put her hair up so she wouldn't have the daunting chore of brushing it.

"You're better than that," Liz said, nodding in Debby's direction.

"I'm sorry, why can't I be friends with Carol and your group? I think I do not understand because your group seems to make everyone think you'll are kind, accepting, and caring," Carol said.

"We are," Liz defended her and the group.

"How can you be if you are telling me to dump a friend who is nothing but kind and caring. She's always been the first person I turn to and confide in. She's her own person and doesn't care what others think. I admire that about her," Carol said.

"I don't care if you are part of the group. The decision is yours, but there's only room for you," Liz said.

The ultimatum thrown down, her hair whipped violently around as she turned her back towards Carol. She walked with her head held high through the library and out the front doors.

Carol's eyes watched the door close, then they turned towards Debby, who was not reading anymore. Looking in all directions, Debby was nowhere to be found. She squinted some as she strained to look in another section of the library.

"Hey, friend," Debby shouted from behind Carol.

After a quick jump and a quick turn in Debby's direction, Carol hissed, "You scared the crap out of me!"

"Thanks for sticking up for me," Debby said.

"What?" Carol asked, cheeks changing to ruby red.

"I was listening, and thank you for defending me. You're my best friend, and I want you to be happy. If your happiness is with them, I will understand," Debby said, straightening her shirt and smoothing her hair.

"I hope YOU understand that our friendship means more to me than trying to fit in with a group, who doesn't accept people for who they are," Carol said. "It's both of us or neither of us. Liz showed me who that group really is and what they are about. I would never be with a group like that. We're friends, and we go together like..."

"Peanut butter and bananas," Debby said.

YOUR TURN:

1. Have you ever been faced with a situation, torn between groups of friends or people?

2. Did Carol make the right decision?

3. Would Debby truly understand if Carol decided to leave her and join the popular group?

4. Define the word steadfast. Does that fit Carol? Explain your answer.

5. Using your answers above, finish the story.

CHAPTER 38
NEW SCHOOL
(Codependent)

"I can't believe you have to move," Joy said. "We just started being best friends."

"I know, I hate this," Gemma said. "My mom and her stupid job." Tears trickled down Gemma's face.

"Here," Joy said. She handed Gemma a tissue and then took one for herself.

"Are you afraid?" Joy asked. "You've moved a lot, but does it get any easier?"

"Not really. This will be my sixth time being the new kid, and I still feel like puking whenever I think about entering the lunchroom," Gemma said.

"Isn't that weird? I've only been the new kid once when I

moved here last year, but it's always the lunchroom that makes my stomach roll over. Why is that?" Joy asked.

"Maybe it's because a sea of people are ready to stare and point at any second. Or the fact that you have to make such an important decision of who to sit with before you even know anyone," Gemma said.

"Right! Totally! Remember when I walked into the lunchroom last year? That was the first time we met. I was terrified," Joy said.

"You didn't look terrified. You just looked like a happy new person with only happy thoughts swirling inside your head," Gemma said.

Joy slid a strand of hair behind her ear and looked at her ring. She twisted it around her finger over and over again. It changed colors, and a deep breath finally escaped her lungs.

"What are you thinking about?" Gemma said. Gemma's eyes were now watching the same thing as Joy's. The ring.

"I've never seen your mood ring change so much," Gemma said. "Why is it doing that?"

"It wants a new owner," Joy said. "It's not really a mood ring. It's a ring that someone gave me. It's a calming ring," Joy said.

"A what?" Gemma asked.

"I don't know who all has had it, but it's clear, it wants you to be its new owner," Joy said.

"I'm feeling lost. This is nothing but a simple mood ring," Gemma said.

"No, actually it's not. I tell people that, but it's so much more," Joy said. "I brought the instructions. I knew it wanted you because of how it's been acting lately when we are together."

"You're freaking me out," Gemma said.

"I know. Just listen. Before I moved here, I was given this ring, and this ring helped me to feel calm and confident. I didn't think it would work because I was like you when I was first given it. But it really does work. You said I looked like I was full of joy when I walked in. It was the ring. Before I put it on that morning, I was a sobbing mess of tears," Joy explained. "I put it on, and I felt so good. I haven't taken it off since."

"Why don't you just keep it? Who cares if it wants a new owner? You keep it," Gemma said.

"The book says if I don't pass it on, bad fortune will come to me," Joy said. "You're leaving is all the bad fortune I can handle. Here, take it."

"I don't think I want to," Gemma said.

"I'm putting it on your dresser. Here are the instructions. You can decide if you want to put it in a box or wear it," Joy said. "It won't hurt you. It just takes the edge off when you have anxiety or need comfort."

Joy placed the ring and the instructions on a white dresser full of flower decals.

After giving Gemma a hug, she stood back and felt a slight tremble in her body. Waves of emotions crashed down on her at once. Tears burst from her eyes, and the sobbing was uncontrollable. She grabbed onto Gemma once more and gave her a bear hug. Tears were spilling onto Gemma's shirt and arm.

"Joy. It's okay. It's going to be okay," Gemma said.

"I know. I know it will. Now that I don't have that ring on, all these emotions are hitting me at once. I have to go. I'm late for dinner," Joy said through the sobs.

"Okay. I'll see you tomorrow," Gemma said.

Joy grabbed the box of tissues, yanked five of them out, and began blotting her eyes. It wasn't stopping the tears, but it would make her shirtless wet. Tucking the box of tissue under her arm, she walked out of Gemma's room.

YOUR TURN:

1. Write the instructions that come with the ring.

2. Do you think Gemma will start wearing the ring? Would you?

3. List the reasons to wear the ring and the reasons to not wear the ring.

4. Define the word codependent. Does that word fit Joy's behavior? Explain your answer.

5. Using your answers above, finish the story.

CHAPTER 39
FISH TRAP
(Piqued)

"I know you're going to ask me something. I can see it in your eyes, so go ahead and ask," Keaton said.

"Okay. Why are you making the holes in the net so small?" Miles asked.

"Because we don't want the fish to escape through them," Keaton explained.

"But we want to catch big fish. Big fish can't escape those holes," Miles said.

"We want all the fish, and we will throw them all back," Keaton said.

"We aren't going to eat them?" Miles asked.

"No," Keaton said.

The net was twice as long as Keaton. A rope was woven between the bigger holes to make two smaller ones. Dirt covered their hands and clothes, but neither took the time to dust them off.

Miles walked around Keaton like he was a referee watching every move, waiting to throw a flag.

"Is that hard?" Miles asked, breaking the silence.

"No, it just takes concentration," Keaton said.

"Oh," Miles said.

Miles bent down and splashed his hands around in the water.

"What are you doing?" Keaton yelled.

"What?" Miles asked, still splashing.

Keaton yanked the back of Miles's shirt, sending them both toppling to the ground.

"You're going to scare all the fish away!" Keaton yelled.

"Sorry," Miles said. He looked at a small rock, grabbed it, and tossed it in the air. He caught it, tossed it again, caught it again.

The onlookers could be heard in the distance as Miles began to throw the rock to the shore on the other side of the lake. The crowd died out quickly as the rock landed only 20 feet from shore, and a harsh stare could be felt from behind.

"Why don't you pick some dandelions for mom. I'm almost done," Keaton said.

"Okay," Miles said. "They can be from both of us."

"Cool," Keaton said. "Be sure to pick them over there, not by the water."

Dandelions littered the area designated for lunch boxes and coats.

"I'm ready, Miles," Keaton said.

Footsteps pounded on the ground at a quick pace, and Miles's hands grabbed the side of the net.

"Just like we practiced, okay," Keaton said.

"Okay," Miles said, smiling from ear to ear.

YOUR TURN:

1. What is the relationship like between these two brothers?

2. What is Keaton's patience level with Miles?

3. How would Keaton's patience change if they were fishing for their dinner versus for fun?

4. Define the word piqued. Does this fit with Keaton's

feelings? Explain your answer.

5. Using your answers, finish the story.

CHAPTER 40
OUT OF HERE
(Arduous)

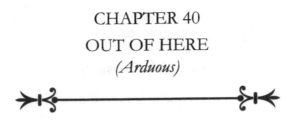

The drive wasn't horrible. It was the relentless traffic that created anger. The view made the route worth it, though.

I'm glad I'm not the bus driver, McKenna thought.

A text message popped up and was just as quickly ignored. A huff of anger mixed into McKenna's thoughts like a blender on high, mixing tainted eggs into the flour. Blonde hair was thrown to one side as her blue eyes watched the mountains slowly rolling by.

Getting off the bus meant she was one step closer to being free for the week. Free from parents, free from responsibilities, and free from other people controlling her. Ten blocks to the west and she would be at Uncle Cody's house. No more worries.

Walking ten blocks wasn't hard. It was hot, but it wasn't too bad. Sunscreen wasn't a consideration at the time she left her house. All she could do was think about a week in the mountains with a group of artsy kids and Uncle Cody leading the way.

"Hey!" she yelled, rounding the corner of the house.

"Hey!" Uncle Cody yelled back. "Your mom has text me like 20 times, asking if you've made it yet. Would you like to respond to her?"

"No," McKenna said.

Cody picked up his phone, took a deep breath, and typed: *She's here, all is good. I'll text you throughout our trip.*

Pushing his phone into his back pocket, he tilted his head to the side and asked, "So?"

"So... what?" McKenna asked. A smirk washed over her lips. She threw her pack into the truck and walked inside the house. "I'm getting a soda. You want one?"

"No," Cody said, shaking his head.

"What's up, Cody?" Lance asked from his car as he parked in the driveway.

"We're almost ready. All the kids are in the house. How was your sermon?" Cody asked.

"Good. Not one person fell asleep this time," Lance said.

They chuckled as Cody gave Lance a hard pat on the back.

"This should be fun," Cody said. "Do you have all your stuff in your truck?"

"Yes, I have everything you told me to get, plus I splurged and got stuff for smores," Lance said.

"Uncle Cody!" McKenna yelled, breaking up the conversation.

"Yeah?" Cody asked.

"I can't find any chips. Do you have chips around here?" McKenna asked.

"Nope. No chips. They're all packed up," Cody said.

YOUR TURN:

1. What is McKenna's relationship like with her parents?

2. Will McKenna experience something life-changing on this trip?

3. Will the time away from her parents change the mood between them when she gets back?

4. Define the word arduous. Does this word fit the story?

Explain your answer.

5. Using your answers, finish the story.

ABOUT THE AUTHOR

Dusty is someone who loves to write. Like all of you readers and writers out there, she loves spending time with her imagination on a regular basis. She hopes that all of her readers will have fun with her books.

CONNECT WITH THE AUTHOR

Website: www.DustyDurston.com

Facebook: https://www.facebook.com/DustyDurston/

Instagram: https://www.instagram.com/dusty_durston/

Pinterest: https://www.pinterest.com/DustyEDurston/

Bookbub: https://www.bookbub.com/profile/dusty-durston?list=about